Hillary was going to marry Ray Saunders, one day, even though so many people seemed to be trying to dissuade her. Her marriage to Clive was over now; he had no bearing on her life any more, no claim to her emotions, and that was how she wanted it . . .

AN ELUSIVE MISTRESS

BY
LINDSAY ARMSTRONG

MILLS & BOON LIMITED
15–16 BROOK'S MEWS
LONDON W1A 1DR

*First published in Great Britain 1986
by Mills & Boon Limited*

© Lindsay Armstrong 1986

*Australian copyright 1986
Philippine copyright 1986
This edition 1986*

ISBN 0 263 75379 4

*Set in Monophoto Times 11 on 11 pt.
01–0686 – 50573*

*Printed and bound in Great Britain by
Collins, Glasgow*

CHAPTER ONE

HILLARY MORRIS stared at her reflection in the mirror and decided there was nothing more she could do. Her hair, as always, lay smooth and thick from a side parting to just above her shoulders and was restrained from falling across her face on the other side by an intricately wrought silver slide. It was that sort of darker fair hair that hairdressers adored because, they said, it showed up highlights or streaks particularly well. Not that Hillary had ever succumbed to this, because one of the things she was stubborn about was her hair. She liked it the way it was.

Her eyes were another sore point, in a sense. An unusual shade of smoky blue, they were inherited from her father, so her mother had often said with a twitch of her well-bred nose. Hillary had never known her father but had come to realise quite young that the mention of him caused her mother a lot of pain. And because she'd loved her mother, she had never pursued the topic of a father who had, apparently, abandoned them both. But she had sometimes wondered if she had also inherited her darker eyebrows from him, and where her heart-shaped face came from.

For the rest of her, her pale, almost translucent skin, her lack of inches—she stood only five feet two in her bare feet—her trim figure, the awful shyness she had suffered from when she was younger, they were all features she had detected in either her mother or her grandparents or her Aunt

Beatrix, who was exactly five feet two, although hardly shy.

'Hillary! Oh, there you are!' A voice disturbed Hillary's contemplation of herself in the mirror and suddenly there were two reflections as Beatrix Selby, who was Hillary's mother's sister, came to stand beside her. 'My dear, you look super!' Bea Selby said. 'Now that's what I call a dress! Ray will want to eat you in that.'

Hillary looked alarmed, then grinned and sat down on the bed in a swirl of smoky-blue lace over a silver taffeta slip. 'Ray's not like that,' she said as she slid on an ankle-strapped silver sandal.

Bea snorted—a thing she did peculiarly effectively, yet very elegantly. In fact she was, in a word, elegant, from the top of her upswept grey hair to the tips of her size four shoes. She was also shrewd, uncannily perceptive and sometimes unforgivably forthright. And, curiously, although she claimed she had been born the ugly duckling—Hillary's mother Marlene had been the pretty one, she often said—she was still a head-turner wherever she went, although now into her fifties. 'It's a question of style,' she'd often said to Hillary, too. 'Style is a more durable thing than prettiness. It's also a question of valuing yourself—something your mother wasn't very good at. Otherwise she wouldn't have let one man turn her bitter and sour. For that matter,' Bea Selby had gone on to say to Hillary on one occasion, 'I firmly believe that no woman should be conned into permitting herself only one man in a lifetime. Because that's where a lot of the trouble starts from. One should sample men like wine. How can you tell a good vintage from the bad, otherwise?'

Since her mother had died and Hillary had come

to live next door to her Aunt Bea, she had become well-acquainted with her aunt's often radical thinking on a variety of subjects. Radical by her mother's standards, certainly, and radical possibly in a woman of Bea Selby's age. But when she had pointed this out once, her aunt had replied placidly that she'd always been way ahead of her time. And if she had practised what she preached regarding men, and she had at least outlived two husbands, she was a glowing advertisement for it, and not only physically. She was always in great demand, did a lot of travelling and had in fact, on this particular evening, been home only a few hours after a trip to Nepal, but was looking as alert as ever.

'If he's not like that—quote unquote,' she said to Hillary's bent head, 'what is he good for?'

Hillary sat up. 'For one thing, Aunt Bea, he doesn't think he's God's gift to women in the physical sense. Which means, in baser terms, that the fact that I haven't gone to bed with him yet has not direly wounded his ego, and that's something I rather admire. It also means we're enjoying a relationship that's not clouded with passion and our judgment of each other is pretty honest, I think.'

'Sounds awful,' Bea said gloomily.

'What's awful about him?' Hillary asked calmly. She stood up and reached for her evening bag. 'He's good-looking . . .'

'Some of the best lovers can be quite ugly,' Bea observed.

'All right,' Hillary conceded with a slight smile. 'I'm sure you're speaking from experience and you're right, good looks have nothing to do with it, but there are other things I like about him very much . . .'

'Not the least his seemingly very tranquil
nature—which, if you ask me, is another way of
saying he's as dull as ditch water—no, don't look
hurt, dear, two can play at being patronising.'

'I wasn't being patronising . . .'

'Yes, you were. And smug! Anyone would think
you were fifty-two instead of twenty-five, to hear
you talk sometimes,' Bea said tartly, then relented
with a grimace. 'Sorry, but I just don't think he's
the right one for you. Are you going to marry
him? I've had this premonition.'

Hillary said after a moment, 'Yes. But not for a
while. We've decided to look for an old house with
a big garden and do it up first.'

'What about the business?' Bea gestured,
because Hillary's home was her place of business
as well.

'Oh, I'll keep it going, naturally. Ray thinks it's
terrific.'

'Who wouldn't?' her aunt replied. 'You're also
quite a trendy figure now. A feather in the cap of
any man.'

'Aunt Bea!' Hillary protested laughingly. 'You
make it sound as if I have to fend prospective
husbands off! I can assure you I don't.'

'That's because you don't try,' said Bea, but
didn't enlarge on this. In fact she took a different
tack. 'What other things do you like about him?
Tell me?'

Hillary sighed, then said with a twinkle in her
eye, 'Who's marrying him? You or me? But if you
must know, we like to do a lot of the same things,
he's patient . . .'

'Then live with him for a while.'

'No.'

'Hillary, do yourself a favour. Don't marry

anyone because he's *patient*. That's not a good enough reason!'

'Aunt Bea,' Hillary said with a suddenly *im*patient look in her eyes which wasn't often there, 'I love you and I know you care about me a great deal, for which I'm very grateful. But nothing you can say will convince me that it's not as good a reason as any other, if not better, to marry someone you like and respect ... Oh,' she said, as a hooter sounded outside, 'there's Ray now. See you!'

And she planted a fond little kiss on her aunt's cheek and left the room in a cloud of Shalimar.

'I was afraid of this,' Bea Selby said to herself, and sighed. She switched off the bedroom light and wandered through to the shop that formed the front part of the little old colonial house she'd bought years ago before the inner Brisbane suburb of Paddington, perched on the foothills of Mount Coot-tha, had begun to enjoy a trendy revival. Now it was becoming an 'in' place to live and many of the lovely old cottages were being restored and were much sought after as prime examples of Queensland colonial architecture. In other words, they were wooden buildings with verandas all round and high-ceilinged, dim rooms that suited the muggy heat of Brisbane well.

It was also a suburb that now boasted a variety of exclusive shops. If you were looking for individual clothes or *objets d'art* or fine foods, nowadays you came to Paddington. And this was one reason why Hillary had been so successful—as someone had envisaged and as her aunt had been forced to concur, at the same time wondering why she hadn't thought of the idea herself.

But she had suggested the project to Hillary four

years ago, after her mother had died. 'Come and live next door to me,' she'd said, 'and open up a shop that sells all the kind of things you like.'

Her niece had looked at her out of those smoky-blue eyes as if she had suggested taking a trip to the moon, but for once Bea Selby had been patient. 'Ever since you were a little girl you've been interested in pottery and china and knick-knacks—things like that. You also used to love digging around in antique shops with Dad ... Anyway, what else did you have in mind? Going back to hotel work?'

And that was what had done it, Bea often mused. That gibe ...

Hillary had started in a small way, selling mainly cottage crafts and antiques. Somehow, Bea had never been quite sure how, Hillary had established a steady source of homemade rugs, patchwork quilts, beautifully hand-embroidered and crocheted table linen, unusual pottery, wall hangings, basketware, enamelware and the like. And she had frequented sales—from garage sales to deceased estate sales—for copper and silverware and small pieces of lovely old cedar furniture, and old jewellery, for all of which, it had turned out, there was a brisk demand.

And she had painted the front shop windows a cinnamon brown with a large, clear, gold-rimmed oval hole in each so that, with the aid of some subtle lighting inside, from the outside one got tantalising glimpses of a jewel-bright rug perhaps, or a lovely old copper kettle or some silver jewellery cascading down a vivid piece of yellow silk.

Hillary had named the shop Pandora's Box.

Then she had branched out in another direction

quite by accident. A wealthy customer, who adored the kind of shop Pandora's Box was, had asked Hillary's advice about redecorating her dining room. And she had found her suggestions so helpful they had gone on to re-do the whole house, for which Hillary, despite her protestations, had received a large fee. But not only that, she had found herself more and more in demand as an interior decorator as word had got around.

Yet with an acumen her aunt hadn't realised she possessed, Hillary had been extremely choosy of her clients and thereby became exclusive. But what had really set the seal of excellence on her work, and made it so sought after, had been the fact that she never pushed any particular style. Instead, she beguiled her clients into remembering the kind of rooms they had admired but been comfortable in, and even if this was an impossible mixture of styles she had the knack of making it come right somehow. And she always rescued their favourite knick-knacks and paintings, even if they were only of sentimental value and most other decorators would have consigned them to the Brisbane River, and found a niche for them.

With the result that no two 'Hillary' rooms looked alike, yet their owners were immensely proud of them. And the *Courier Mail* had done a feature spread on her after she had decorated the interior of a beautiful old house which had been restored and converted to a restaurant and had been named simply Hillary's, after her.

And she had become drawn, accordingly, more and more into the kind of social circles Ray Saunders moved in—the kind of circles that Bea Selby had laughed delightedly to hear once described as the Sloane Ranger set of Brisbane, forgetting perhaps that she too had long held a kind of court in the same circles. 'But I've never denied,' she'd said, still laughing when Hillary had pointed this out to her, 'that it's the epitome of the private school, old school tie snobbery kind of thing. I mean, you only have to listen to them behind the stand at Ballymore on a Sunday afternoon to realise that!'

Ballymore was the centre of rugby union in Queensland. It was, too, apparently, the heart of Brisbane high society. None of your essentially Aussie ockers frequented the stands of Ballymore. And the one question that was invariably asked of newcomers, of Hillary's age and younger anyway, was, what school had you attended? In fact Hillary had been to the right school but she'd missed out on the immediate post-school era of Ballymore ...

Mind you, she's handled it well, Bea Selby mused to herself ... And came out of her reverie to see, out of the shop window, her niece being helped into a small, navy-blue Alfa Romeo that always sounded to her as if it was driven by a sewing machine ...

Bea hitched one shoulder irritably, thinking that this was just another facet of Ray Saunders that irritated her so—a grown man who still delighted in supremely uncomfortable little sports cars. And she turned away with another sigh and let herself out of Hillary's house and into her own next door.

Curiously, Hillary was thinking something similar—about cars anyway as she tried to arrange her dress so that it wouldn't be impossibly crushed. And thinking about men who seemed so grown up most of the time, until it came to cars. But contrary to the spirit of irritation it engendered in

her aunt, she mostly found it rather endearing. Yet
tonight, possibly because she was working rather
hard on the endearing aspect of it and trying not
to visualise herself arriving at one of the premier
balls of the season—for all that it was a party
do—all wrinkled, she was quieter than normal.

Which prompted Ray Saunders to drop his arm
around her shoulders and say, 'Anything wrong?'

'No. Why?'

'I don't know.' He had to take his arm away to
change gear. 'Looking forward to tonight?'

'Mmm.'

'It's always a great night. Last year we danced
until dawn and then went to the Breakfast Creek
for bacon and eggs. Hillary . . .' His voice changed
and she turned her head to look at him. 'Will you
let me do something tonight? Will you let me
announce our engagement?'

She took a breath and stared into his blue eyes.
Funnily enough, she sometimes thought, they had
very similar colouring . . . Wouldn't do for us to
have any dark-eyed children, she'd thought rather
frivolously once. It would be a dead give-away,
wouldn't it, Mendel?

She said, 'Ray, I thought we'd agreed to do it all
very quietly.'

He hesitated, as if searching for the right words.
'You wanted to do it that way and I agreed. But
now I'm finding it a little hard not to shout it from
the roof tops. And I can't think of any real reason
why we shouldn't at least let everyone know we're
engaged. It would change nothing else, Hillary,' he
said levelly.

She was silent, knowing what he meant, that he
wouldn't try to pressure her to sleep with him until
they were married. And all of a sudden she found

herself feeling unreasonable, as if she was asking too much of him, taking unfair advantage of him . . .

'All right,' she said. 'Yes, let's.'

He put his arm around her again. 'Thanks,' he said, a little huskily. 'Mum and Dad agree with me, by the way. They're delighted at the prospect of having you as a daughter-in-law and want to tell the world, too.'

But instead of being delighted in return at Mum and Dad's sentiments, Hillary, as always when she thought of the senior Saunders, was conscious of an element of nervousness. For there was something curiously intimidating about Ray's parents. In fact sometimes she couldn't help wishing he had none: well, not such prominent ones anyway.

Charles Saunders was a millionaire industrialist and also a state president of the political party whose annual fund-raising ball they were attending tonight. And Ray, who had a senior position in the family buisness which, his father was fond of saying, he'd thoroughly earned, was proposing to go into politics, too, although in a more direct manner than his father. He was planning to stand for State Parliament.

Hillary didn't object to this *per se*. But she did sometimes find herself questioning the way it was being done. It was as if Ray's father vetted everything he did with an eye to whether it would be beneficial to his future career. And she couldn't help wondering whether *she'd* been thoroughly vetted, with a column for ticks and a column for crosses against her, to see if she would make a suitable wife for a politician—perhaps a future premier of the state?

But the ticks must have outweighed the crosses, she'd told herself once, and fallen to wondering if she wanted to be the wife of a premier and if she could ever hope to emulate the style of Ray's mother Irene, who was the epitome of charm and fearsomely capable of organising things—tonight's ball being just one example.

Two other things troubled her slightly. One was the recent whisper of an up-coming by-election in a party blue ribbon seat for which, with his party background, Ray would be assured of pre-selection and, because of the nature of the electorate, assured of winning it. It just seems too easy, Hillary had thought, and then suffered a pang of guilt. The other thing was that she couldn't help wondering sometimes if anyone had stopped to think that Ray might just not be cut out to be a future premier. Because all the qualities she loved about him—his kindness, his gentleness and patience—were none of the things his dynamic father was especially knwon for, although they looked quite a lot alike, both being tall and broad-shouldered and impressive of presence . . .

She spoke suddenly as the Alfa ducked into a parking space. 'When? I mean before dinner, after dinner—when will you do it?'

'About half-way through, I should think. Don't be nervous,' he said softly, and kissed her with both his arms around her.

She closed her eyes and rested against him and felt so safe, somehow, she took a breath and vowed to be everything he could possibly want her to be tonight.

Dinner came and went and the thousand or so people in the ballroom began to dance as the band struck up, and to circulate away from their long, white-dressed dinner tables each with its gladioli decoration, and to form splinter groups.

Hillary danced with Ray and then his father, who complimented her on how she looked but made no mention of the engagement. And she sat for a time with his mother, who said nothing about it either but insisted for the first time that Hillary called her Irene.

And she and Ray made the rounds of the people they knew, which were many, and almost without exception they told her her how lovely she looked and how they were dying to get their houses or units redecorated *à la* Hillary.

It began to get quite hot in the ballroom as people loosened up and the band became a bit more daring. And it was when Hillary was dancing with a courteous old gentleman who, it turned out, was the Speaker of the House that her steps faltered as she stared at the retreating back of a woman in a scarlet dress. But it wasn't the dress she was staring at, nor the sinuous back it partly enclosed, it was at the hand that lay lightly on the woman's waist, a tanned, long-fingered hand . . .

Then the couple were swallowed up in the colourful throng and Hillary's partner stared at her and said with some concern, 'My dear, are you all right? You look a bit pale. Should we stop and get a drink perhaps?'

'I . . . Thank you, that sounds lovely. It's become a bit of a crush, hasn't it?'

Her cavalier agreed and steered her solicitously towards her table where he flagged down a passing waiter and hi-jacked from his tray a long, cool drink bound for someone else.

'Don't normally pull rank,' he said to Hillary with a twinkle in his eye, 'but this is an exception. How do you feel now?'

'I'm fine,' said Hillary sincerely and gratefully. 'It was just . . .'

'I know!' He waved a hand and went on talking, not realising he was talking to himself. Because Hillary was saying to herself, it was just imagination, thank God! Yet she couldn't help herself from looking again for that scarlet dress, only to realise that there could be a hundred scarlet dresses easily . . .

Then Ray arrived and they sat with the Speaker for a while, chatting until others joined them and they regrouped, and she found herself feeling quite normal again. So that when Ray glanced at his watch and asked her with a grin to dance, she stood up with no hesitation.

But they hadn't been on the floor long when the lights went out to a roll of drums and the rest of the dancers seemed to melt away, although Ray wouldn't allow her to follow. Then a single spotlight came on, capturing just the two of them on the empty floor . . .

Hillary blinked and a subsidiary light came on, capturing this time, she saw as she turned her head, Ray's father on the band's dais with a microphone in his hand, and she thought, oh no, not like this!

But like this it was obviously going to be, and with Ray's connivance . . .

'Dear friends,' Charles Saunders said sonorously, but Hillary didn't really hear what else he said because she was thinking furiously, a thousand friends! Oh no, more like a thousand of the party faithful and a golden opportunity to turn an engagement into a political event! Why did I agree to this? Because I foolishly thought Ray would make a little speech at our table perhaps and leave it at that. But *this* . . .

'. . . and I'd like to welcome Hillary into our family, and to express Irene's and my joy at our son's engagement to a lovely girl. I give you Ray and Hillary!'

'Ray and Hillary!' the crowd echoed enthusiastically, and raised primed glasses as the band struck up . . . For they are jolly good fellows!

But the most impossible thing of all was that Ray was actually pleased, Hillary could tell, as he turned her towards him and reached into his pocket to withdraw a diamond ring which he slid on to her nerveless finger. Then he bent his head and kissed her and swung her into his arms as flashlights popped frenziedly—the press had obviously been primed too—and the band slid into a slow waltz.

'This,' she said through her teeth, 'is what you do at weddings, Ray!'

But he only grinned down at her and gathered her closer so that she had no option but to dance. 'Did your father . . . Was it all his idea, Ray?'

'Don't be cross, darling. I promise you that from now on it will be as quiet and secret as you want. But I told you how I felt. I love you, Hillary,' he said quietly as they danced in solitary splendour. 'I can't *hide* that any longer.'

'But . . .' she said, then bit her lip. How to tell him that her very soul cringed from this kind of . . . manipulation and exposure? Because she had no doubt that was what it was. Another step up the ladder of Ray Saunders' carefully orchestrated, budding public-image building campaign. How to do it when he was looking down at her so honestly with his heart in his eyes?

And she closed her eyes suddenly and laid her head on his shoulder and felt his heart beating beneath it as their audience applauded more loudly than ever and a few even had the temerity to whistle . . .

Oh, Ray, she thought, I love you, too, but . . .

Then it was over. Perhaps the bandleader had taken pity on her and curtailed the waltz, or others had taken pity on her and decided to join in, but suddenly Ray was pushing his way off the floor with her hand in his and leading her to the bar where his father and mother were waiting with a bottle of champagne, French, in a silver bucket between them, and they kissed Hillary and so did a lot of other people until Ray said laughingly, 'Hey! Fair go. Enough's enough!' and put his arm about her waist protectively.

Which had produced a slight lull in the festivities, Hillary noted, as she sipped champagne and thought how she hated it, especially French, which seemed to be twice as sour to her.

But the lull didn't last long. Out of the corner of her eye, Hillary caught a flash of scarlet and then, with no other warning, found herself staring up into the mocking grey eyes of a tall man who wore his dinner suit beneath slightly untamed, thick fair hair, with the air of someone supremely at home in it.

And the world seemed to stop and she spilt some champagne down her dress as he said to her, 'Hillary, congratulations. This is a surprise!'

She opened her mouth and closed it like a fish out of water and could only stare at the man who had addressed her with stunned eyes as she thought chaotically, it *was* his hand! And the wearer of the scarlet dress was standing beside him—a gorgeous brunette of about thirty perhaps.

Hillary blinked, hoping she was in the grip of a nightmare. But nothing went away. In fact, the tall man turned to her prospective father-in-law and proceeded to introduce himself . . .

'I don't believe we've met, sir—ma'am,' he said easily, and inclined his head towards Irene Saunders, 'but I'm Clive Eastman.' His lips twisted as a collective gasp of recognition went up and Charles Saunders put out his hand genially. He went on, taking the hand, 'How do you do? I'm also Hillary's ex-husband, but I suppose you know that.'

There were about twenty people in earshot and the shock waves that reverberated through them were almost deafening in an entirely silent way. Ray's hand tightened on Hillary's waist and his expression was stunned and angry.

But this was a mild reaction compared to the tinge of purple that entered his father's cheeks and the way he snatched his hand away as his features, in a mesmerising manner, literally seemed to swell . . .

And for once in her life, Irene Saunders was caught doing a double-take, caught for posterity by a press camera-man still hovering hopefully. For the rest of the group, they all seemed to sport suddenly avid expressions of pop-eyed expectancy.

All of which caused Clive Eastman to raise his eyebrows and look genuinely amused, and to turn back to Hillary and say quizzically, 'Didn't you tell them about me, darling?'

'I . . . Yes,' she heard herself saying hoarsely.

'No, you didn't!' Charles Saunders countered through his teeth.

'I told Ray I'd been married before and . . .'

'Not to this man,' Charles barked at her furiously, his features contorted. 'Not to . . . this fiddle-playing womaniser!'

'Dad, she did,' Ray intervened uncomfortably. 'She told me but I . . .'

'You idiot!' his father snapped, and shook off Irene's warning hand on his arm. 'You told me her first marriage was of no account, that she'd been so young it was a mistake you could forgive anyone for . . .'

'She was very young,' Clive Eastman said helpfully, but Charles Saunders was in full spate.

'You told me it was useless to dig up the dirt on a teenage marriage . . .'

'I told you,' Ray's voice was suddenly different from how it had ever sounded to Hillary, 'that I loved her and I was going to marry her whether you dug up a *mountain* of dirt. And I meant it . . .'

'Oho! And how do you think it's going to look when the world knows—which they surely will now—who she was married to before? A rake and a libertine. A . . .' But his fury was so great he couldn't go on.

Which was possibly unfortunate as it turned out, because it gave Clive Eastman a chance to retaliate as Hillary knew he would, and she trembled visibly.

'My dear Hillary,' he said to her, his eyes slightly narrowed which was a sign she knew from old and feared, 'I can't believe you've willingly got yourself into this. I mean, I wasn't going to mention it, but the unbelievable kitschness—for want of a better word—of that engagement announcement just didn't seem like you at all. Or is it that you've become a party cadre too? Dear me!'

Hillary made a strangled sound, but it seemed he wasn't quite finished because he turned to Ray then and said lazily, 'Speaking as the person who had the pleasure of ... breaking Hillary in, you might say, I must congratulate *you* on your taste, though, old chap. She's very lovely, lovelier if anything now.' He glanced at Hillary critically. 'And I'm sure you'll find I did a good job, if you haven't already done so,' he added gently.

The silence was dreadful. But in Hillary's mind there was no such silence, there was a growing, clamouring fury and curiously, perhaps ridiculously, a line from a current popular song ... Oh no, I got to keep on moving ...

'You bastard,' she said conversationally, and dashed the contents of her champagne glass into his face.

But she knew she'd done the wrong thing immediately. Knew it through the sudden turmoil that surrounded them—Charles Saunders' violent movement as another flashbulb popped, people moving embarrassedly away, Irene's little moue of despair, Ray's shock—yet knew it for none of these reasons, as Clive only grinned devilishly and calmly reached for his handkerchief to wipe his face.

He *wanted* to provoke me, she thought despairingly. But *why*?

CHAPTER TWO

'BROUGHT you some breakfast, Hillary,' Bea Selby said quite late the following morning.

Hillary opened her eyes unwillingly. 'Thanks,' she murmured sleepily then sat up abruptly. 'Oh God . . .'

'I know.'

She turned to her aunt. 'You can't possibly know . . . You do. It's not,' she closed her eyes briefly , 'in the papers?'

'No.'

'Then . . .?'

'I've had at least six phone-calls this morning. Eat your egg. You,' Bea grinned suddenly, 'were magnificent, by the sound of things.'

Hillary dug into her boiled egg distractedly 'No, I wasn't. I only made things worse. Which was what he wanted me to do!'

'Hillary,' her aunt drew up a chair beside the bed, and said earnestly, 'it's exactly what I would have done, what most people would have done! What are you worried about? Oh, don't tell me! Ray's image, the party image. But good God, girl, you're not even married to him yet!'

'You don't understand . . .'

'I understand one thing,' Bea said vigorously, 'if you're going to allow them to make you into a perfect little party wife like Irene Saunders is, you're less of a person than I took you for. I have never subscribed to the theory that people have to bury all their spontaneous emotions for

23

the greater good of . . .'

'Neither do I, normally,' Hillary interrupted wearily. 'And if you think I enjoyed being put under a spotlight literally like that, last night, you're wrong. And if you think I don't *hate* Charles Saunders now, and his nasty little clichés about digging up the dirt . . .' Angry tears glimmered in her eyes. 'I always suspected he was the type who'd have dossiers on people. But,' she sighed and brushed away the tears, 'Ray's different. He's just as much a victim of his father as . . . I am.'

'Then let him unvictimise himself,' said Bea a little acidly. 'He's a grown man, after all.'

'He doesn't see it quite that way.'

'Perhaps he will now—after last night.'

There was silence as Hillary finished her boiled egg and sipped her tea. Then they both spoke together.

'Clive . . .'

Bea looked at Hillary's down-bent head. 'Go on. Tell me about him.'

Hillary traced the fluted edge of her teacup for a time. 'He hasn't changed,' she said finally, and lifted her head. 'Did you know he was back?'

'No . . . But then Brisbane is his home town.'

'He was right. It was all so . . . kitsch. But I'll never forgive him for what he said afterwards. Or for . . . creating the whole incident in the first place.'

'Or yourself for letting him get to you?' Bea said wisely after a time.

'I suppose so,' whispered Hillary. Then she added helplessly. 'But why do a thing like that? Talking of kitsch,' a note of anger entered her voice, 'surely it's the height of bad taste to . . . to parade yourself in front of your former wife and her fiancé at their engagement? It's not as if we parted the best of friends.'

'Clive was always a little like that, if I recall,' Bea said meditatively.

'He was always impossible,' Hillary agreed coldly.

'And you were very much in love with him once, my dear.' There was something oddly challenging in Bea Selby's eyes.

'I was infatuated,' Hillary said tiredly. 'Dazzled. I couldn't believe he could be interested in someone like me. And I was too young to know any better. But I soon learnt.'

'All the same, he married you.'

'Oh yes. You know why? He told me once . . . He said he'd discovered he had some scruples he didn't realise he possessed.'

'Hillary . . .'

'And do you know what he actually said last night?' Hillary went on. 'He . . . he . . .'

'I know. I'm afraid to say a lot of other people do, too, or will do sooner or later. It was unforgivable. Er . . . What happened afterwards?'

'I'm surprised you don't know that,' Hillary said bitterly. 'Ray and his father had a row, Ray brought me home swearing all the way that nothing could make him love me any less and trying to make me promise that if Clive tried to so much as look at me again, I would tell him so that he could personally flatten him . . .'

Bea laughed a little. 'I would have thought he'd had his opportunity to do that and missed it. Perhaps he's going to be a better politician than we imagine. All talk . . . Sorry, darling, I didn't mean that.'

'But that's another thing you don't understand!' Hillary said agitatedly. 'Clive has . . . I don't know how to explain it, but he has this facility for getting the better of people. He actually, although he was entirely in the wrong last night—we're agreed on that, aren't we?—well, he actually walked away leaving us all standing there looking so small and foolish.'

'Ah, but that's the point I was trying to make earlier, Hillary. Why did *you* feel small and foolish? There was no need . . .'

'There was every need,' Hillary answered. 'You try hearing yourself talked of as being broken in like a . . . a horse and being passed on to a new m-master! I've never been so humiliated in my life,' she said, with tears now streaming down her face. 'And that's just what he wanted me to feel because . . . because . . . oh, go away, Aunt Bea,' she commanded. 'Just leave me alone!'

Bea Selby looked as if she was in two minds for a moment. Then she complied, taking the breakfast tray with her.

Hillary lay back as the door closed behind her aunt and battled angrily with her tears, recalling vividly the vow she had once made never to shed another tear over Clive Eastman. Well, she had kept that vow for nearly six years until now, but than she hadn't seen him for nearly six years . . . until last night.

Let's hope it's twice as long before I see him again, she thought. Let's hope it's never again. Broken in . . .Oh, what an innocent I must have been to him!

And her thoughts slipped back, although this was also something she had vowed never to do to herself again. But she couldn't help herself, she found . . .

*   *   *

She had been barely eighteen, only six months out of school and a trainee receptionist at a posh Brisbane hotel, when she had first met Clive Eastman. It wasn't the career her mother had particularly wanted for her, but her grandfather, for once, had overruled her mother. He had said that the tourist industry was the fastest growing in Queensland and that he thought Hillary would be good at dealing with people.

'But she's so shy!' Marlene Morris had objected.

'*I* know, because it's something I've battled with all my life,' Hillary's adored grandfather had said, 'but this will help her to overcome it. And she has other qualities that will stand her in good stead, I think. She's reliable, meticulous . . . And you, my dear, are turning up your nose at this opportunity because you're a bit of a snob!' he'd added.

Hillary had taken the job and been utterly miserable for the first couple of months. Not only *was* she terribly shy, she had also led an amazingly protected life. Her mother had seen to that and not permitted even Hillary's grandfather to overrule her in this. She had never had a boyfriend and, such was the cocoon her mother had wrapped her in, never really thought about rebelling against it. With the result that, even at her all-girls' school, her peers had regarded her as something of an anomaly, but she hadn't worried much about that either. Life at home had been enough for her. She and her mother had lived with her grandparents for as long as she could remember in their big comfortable house, and they had lacked for nothing. As for companionship, her best friend had always been her grandfather and they had gone to concerts together and the cricket and they'd collected stamps together, and after her grandmother had died, they were closer than ever.

With the result that not even the sometimes amazingly sophisticated talk she heard at school, or the slightly shocking confidences she was often on the receiving end of—she was quietly popular even for a freak—prepared her for being thrust into a society where no one cared what she overheard, and she didn't have her mother at her side to freeze the passes that were made at her, or for that matter, because she couldn't bring herself to mention them, her grandfather to explain that not everyone was as reserved as they were.

But she had struggled on, still wearing her mother's choice of clothes which were prim in the extreme, and because her grandfather had been right, she was reliable and meticulous and also tenacious beneath that shy exterior, the management had been pleased with her and she had been given more and more responsible jobs which had boosted her confidence a lot.

And as had happened at school, she had become quietly popular and gradually the staff at the hotel, who collectively enjoyed testing out new recruits, had become collectively protective of Hillary Morris, to their astonishment...

Particularly Wendy Fenton who was head lady receptionist. 'Don't swear like that in front of her,' she'd said ferociously one day to Mike Pearson who was head porter and considered himself irresistible to women. 'You only do it to make her blush!'

'I like the way she blushes.'

'I *know*, but she's only a baby. Come on, Mike, give the kid a break!'

The kid had been there for six months when

Clive Eastman had descended on Brisbane for three concerts, the first he had ever given in his home state. The venue had been Her Majesty's Theatre, which was now defunct apart from the façade, and the staff at the hotel had been blasé because they handled most of the superstars who came to Brisbane. Clive Eastman had shaken them out of that world-weary mood rather spectacularly.

'He is mad. For one thing, the man is mad,' the hotel manager was heard to say quite early on in the proceedings. And his distraught look, so unlike the usually dignified Mr Luigi who had managed hotels all around the world, had given proof to this statement. Because despite being Italian, he was normally the soul of dignified calmness, so dignified, Hillary was tempted to curtsy whenever he infrequently passed by.

'Oh, I don't mind,' Mr Luigi went on plaintively to Wendy Fenton, 'taking the blame for things which are not my fault—in fact it helps when you are dealing with the artistic temperament.' He rolled his eyes significantly. 'However, I have never before been threatened with being tossed over the balcony. No, not ever before. And mind you, only over the matter of a lost shirt! Which was lost, moreover, not in the hotel laundry nor by the valet service . . . He has this one favourite shirt to perform in, only one. You wouldn't believe it possible, would you? To be a violinist of such note, to be now being compared to a young Menuhin, yet to have only one shirt to perform in? It makes no sense.'

'Where was it?' Wendy enquired.

'Rolled up in a ball in his suitcase. Of course we did an express laundry job on it. We never bear grudges,' Mr Luigi said gloomily. 'However,' he brightened fractionally, 'he played like an angel. Mendelssohn ... I was transported,' he added honestly.

'You mean you *went*—after narrowly escaping being tossed over the balcony?' Wendy was incredulous.

'He gave me a ticket—one of the best. I went. He was superb. He is obviously a genius. Unfortunately,' Mr Luigi added nervously, 'we have him for four more days. Therefore I implore you, Miss Fenton, to exercise your greatest tact and caution in any dealings with him and to see that your subordinates do too.'

'Look here, kids,' Wendy was heard to say, following her conversation with Mr Luigi, to that part of the staff she was responsible for, 'we have a nut staying, in case you hadn't already gathered. He plays the violin and throws people around as well. He's a maddo, but we aren't going to let on. In fact, we're going to treat him as if he was King Solomon, right? Right. And if you do happen to come up against him and things look as if they might get out of hand, come to me.' She stuck her jaw out. 'I've had considerable experience of nuts.'

For personal reasons, much of the hullabaloo surrounding Clive Eastman escaped Hillary. And it was quite by chance that at lunchtime of the third day of his six-day stay, she was sent up to his suite armed with a notepad and pencil to take some dictation from him. The hotel provided secretarial services to its guests and this was Wendy's responsibility. However, when the call came Wendy was at lunch, the secretarial pool was discovered to be seriously depleted for a variety of reasons, and in the ensuing scramble, Mr Luigi lined up everyone else in reception at the time, to discover that only Hillary could do shorthand.

'It will have to be you, then, Miss Morris,' he said worriedly.

'I have filled in before,' Hillary offered.

'Good. But ...Oh well, it will have to be you. Off you go then, Miss Morris ...'

'You sent Hillary!' Wendy Fenton all but shouted when she got back from lunch ten minutes later. 'That's like sending a shorn lamb to the slaughter!'

'I've observed Miss Morris lately, Miss Fenton, and I think she's developing a nice way of handling people.'

'People, yes! Mad musicians who are also ladykillers, in case you hadn't noticed ...'

'There was no one else,' Mr Luigi said pacifically. 'Besides, talking of shorn lambs, isn't there a saying that they temper the wind?'

Wendy stared at him. 'Are you sure ... that sounds wrong! Isn't it that the shorn lamb needs to be tempered *from* the wind?'

Mr Luigi shrugged. 'Possibly. English is not my native tongue and sometimes I get things confused. But I have faith in Miss Morris, anyway,' he added majestically. And as it turned out, he was right in a way ...

'Who are you?' Clive Eastman demanded in reply to Hillary's knock.

She took a breath as she stared up at the tall man who stood in the doorway and had to steel herself, strangely, not to turn away and take flight. Because there was a barely suppressed dynamism in every inch of him from his thin, vital, arrogantly moulded face downwards through his lithe,

beautifully proportioned body. But at that particular moment it was more, it was an irate,
impatient dynamic impact he exuded.

Hillary swallowed and said politely, 'I'm from
reception, sir. I've come to take your dictation.'

He looked her up and down, noting the tartan
skirt she wore with a navy-blue pullover, the lace-
edged collar of her blouse exposed neatly. She also
wore neat navy-blue court shoes with a tiny heel
and her hair was clipped back on one side, as
always, with a blue slide. She would come, Clive
Eastman found himself thinking unexpectedly, just
about up to my heart . . .

He said, 'You could have fooled me. You look
like a refugee from boarding school.'

'Oh, I've worked here for six months now, sir,'
she assured him anxiously, 'and . . . shorthand was
one of my best subjects.'

Clive Eastman studied her earnest expression for
a moment, then he smiled suddenly, a peculiarly
sweet smile that took most people by surprise and
quite bowled them over, too.

'Very well, ma'am,' he said, and stood aside for
her to enter. 'To be quite honest I think I prefer a
pocket-sized version of the real thing . . . Where
would you like to sit?'

He established her comfortably, then went to
stand at the french windows that led on to the
balcony, from where there was a superb view of
the Brisbane River. He was silent for a time,
staring out, then he turned back and said, 'I want
to write two letters. One to my agent in London,
and one to my accountant. I'm sacking them
both.'

Hillary blinked and looked startled.

'I'll give you the addresses later. Dear Ned,' he

began, 'he's my agent . . . Dear Ned . . . Thanks to
your latest c . . . foul-up, I am in the position of
being out of work for the next three months . . .'
He pulled a hand out of his pocket and scratched
his head. 'I wouldn't mind so much . . . if this
wasn't the latest in a long line of . . . What on
earth's the matter?' he demanded irritably, as he
noticed that Hillary was no longer writing but
staring at him with unmistakable tears in her eyes.
'Am I going too fast?'

'N-no . . .'

'Then—You don't have to feel sorry for bloody
Ned.'

'It's not that,' she whispered miserably. 'I don't
even know him,' she added with a watery smile
and her pencil poised again. 'I'm sorry. Please go
on.'

'How can I go on? Or is this your normal
practice?'

'No . . .'

'So?' he said impatiently.

Hillary's lips trembled. 'It's your watch,' she
said unhappily. 'It's the same kind I gave to my
grandfather for his sixtieth birthday. He . . . he
died last week. The silly thing is . . . I haven't been
able to cry, although I loved him so much. He was
my best friend . . .'

Clive Eastman stared at her as she bowed her
head and her slim, girlish shoulders started to
shake uncontrollably.

I don't believe this, he thought, as he watched
Hillary desperately try to take a grip on herself
then, and stand up unsteadily.

'If . . . if you'll excuse me for a moment,' she
gulped, 'I'll wash my face . . .'

And that was when he was possessed of an

unexpected impulse, this time. 'Now you've
started,' he said matter-of-factly, 'you might as
well get it over with. Started crying, I mean. Here.'
He moved over to her, took the notebook and
pencil from her and put them down, and drew her
into his arms. 'Consider me in the nature of a
providential shoulder to cry on. Now I come to
think of it, I loved my great-grandfather very
much, too.'

Hillary wept unrestrainedly for about five
minutes and he didn't say any more, just held
her childish figure gently and reflected that he'd
been right, she didn't come much above his
heart . . .

Then she stopped and sniffed and laid her cheek
on the wet patch her tears had left on his shirt, and
said huskily, 'I'm so very sorry.'

'That's all right.'

'You probably think I'm mad . . .'

'Not at all. Feel better?'

'I . . . Yes,' she said a little wonderingly. 'He did
say I wasn't to be sad, but . . .'

'I know. That's easier said than done. Have you
had any lunch?'

'No. I don't go off for another hour.'

'Then have some with me.' He let her go.

'Oh, I couldn't! Besides, the letters . . .'

Clive Eastman grinned. 'We'll do 'em later.'
And oblivious to her look of shock, he strode over
to the phone and ordered lunch for two.

'Don't worry about it,' he said, as he put the
phone down and observed her twisting her hands
uncertainly. 'Mr Luigi has repeatedly assured me
that every facility of this fine hotel is at my
disposal. Why should that exclude you?'

Six months ago Hillary would have read nothing

much into this, but some harsh experience had taught her to look for the guard against hidden meanings, and she blushed suddenly.

Which caused Clive Eastman to raise his eyebrows and then say wryly, 'I didn't mean it in that way. I just . . . don't like having lunch on my own. Tell you what, I'll get your boss's approval.' And he reached for the phone again to do just that with no idea of the acute consternation he was causing in reception . . .

'A working lunch?' Wendy Fenton said into her private hot line to Mr Luigi. 'Is that what he said? Well, I'll tell you what, if she isn't back in an hour, I shall personally go up and check this working lunch out!'

However, the next hour proved to be extremely pleasant for Hillary. She ate smoked salmon and a delicious chicken fricassee, although she declined the wine, and in the process heard an expurgated edition of Clive Eastman's life which had fascinated her. Not that he'd intended to tell her his life story, he stopped to think once, ruefully, but in an effort to put her at her ease he had started to tell her about his great-grandfather.

'So you're half Russian?' she said, wide-eyed.

'Oh no—eighth at most. He married an Australian of Cornish descent and had ten children, one of whom was my grandpa. *He* married an Australian, too, and had my mother, who married an Australian as well, as my father.'

'And your great-grandfather came here after the Russian Revolution? What did he do?' she asked.

'Took up cane-farming near Mackay. I still have dozens of relatives up there.'

'Did he play the violin?'

'Yes, he did. That's how I got started—and for a

long time rued the day. I'd have much rather been a horse trainer—I'm still crazy about horses.'

Hillary looked puzzled.

'Well, it was like this . . .' And that was how he had got started on his boyhood and, for the first time for a long time, relived some of the agonies of it. Of being the bone of contention between his parents, who hadn't taken long to discover they weren't soulmates; of being something of a child prodigy and how his father had thought it was 'cissy' to play the violin while his mother had doggedly scrimped and saved for his lessons; of the awful day when he was sixteen and he'd knocked his father to the floor to prove he was a man. In fact it hadn't been only his father's disapproval he'd felt and in his late teens he had spent a lot of time demonstrating how tough he was—to the despair of his mother who had worried dreadfully about his hands. He had also, again to the despair of his mother, gone out of his way to be the local Romeo . . . but perhaps that came naturally, he thought with an inward grin as he sat across the table from Hillary.

But in fact he had several times sworn to give the violin up and had. Only his great-grandfather had talked him out of it. And unexpectedly, an old nun who had been one of his first teachers. She had tapped another torment within him and talked to him of it. 'It's like a mistress,' she had said. 'Wayward, elusive sometimes, drives you mad, then gives you more pleasure than anything. That's how the best mistresses are—that's how your art is to you. And that's what will make it great. Perfection is also pain.'

Hillary thought about this for a while, after he had told her—and, incidentally, wondered if he should have left this bit out, too, as he'd left out the bit of being the local Romeo. Then she said surprisingly, 'I think she must have been very wise.'

'She was. In the literal sense too, I've since discovered, although where she got that bit of wisdom from, heaven knows!' He grinned faintly, but as Hillary started to colour he sobered and went on to tell her about his life overseas after winning a scholarship, and the great highlight . . . winning the Tchaikovsky Gold Medal.

'So it was all worth it?' Hillary said shyly.

He stared at her. 'Yes,' he said after a time, 'it was.'

They were silent together for a while, a strangely companionable silence. Then Hillary suddenly caught sight of her notebook and pencil, and remembered what she was there for really.

'Oh,' she said, and looked guiltily at her watch. 'Well, I'll work through my lunch hour, of course.' She reached for the pad. 'Let's see, we got up to . .'

But Clive Eastman stretched and laughed. 'Forget about them,' he drawled. 'I've changed my mind.'

'You mean —you aren't going to sack them any more?'

'Actually, there's no point. I've sacked Ned every six months, roughly, since I've known him. He never takes the hint. Well,' he grimaced, 'put it this way. Ned can see through to my soul in some uncanny way. He knows when I just need to let off steam.'

'But you said you were out of work for three months . . . because of him.'

'He probably thinks I need a break. Which I do.

And where better to take it than Queensland, the Sunshine State, for that matter my home?' But there was something rather dry in the way he said it that caused Hillary to look at him uncertainly.

'You don't like Queensland?'

'I'm afraid, my dear ... By the way, I don't even know your name.'

She told him.

'Hillary,' he said experimentally. 'I've never known a Hillary ... What was I saying? Oh yes, I'm afraid I've become one of those awful breed of people—a jet-setter who can't stay in one place long, least of all the wilds of the southern hemisphere. But it's what I should do. Try to get back to the basics. My soul feels as if it needs it even if the intellect is unwilling. I suspect that's why Ned arranged the tour this way up, with Brisbane last. I suspect he was trying to tell me something. That's why I got mad.'

'There are some nice places here,' said Hillary a little self-consciously.

'Spoken like a true Queenslander!' he replied with a grin, then his eyes softened. 'And you're right, there are some lovely places. I just wish I had someone like ...' He stopped and thought, dear God, I must be going mad! She's only a little girl ...

Hillary stood up awkwardly. 'I'd better be going. Thank you very much for the lunch.'

'A pleasure,' he murmured, and stood up himself. 'One day, when it's not so raw any more, you must tell me about your grandfather.'

'Thank you, I'd like to,' she said tremulously, but smiled to show him she wasn't in any danger of breaking down, because it did seem that, although the sadness remained, the acute grief in at

last finding expression, no longer seemed like a
bottomless pit.

Then, because she didn't know how to say
goodbye in any way that didn't seem gauche, she
just left quietly.

To find Wendy Fenton hovering outside.

'What have you been doing?' demanded Wendy,
once Hillary had closed the door.

'Nothing. I ... er ... He asked me to have
lunch with him. But he did ring Mr Luigi ...'

'I know. But why did he want to have lunch
with you?'

'Well ...' And that was the first time Hillary
Morris experienced the incredibly difficult task of
explaining Clive Eastman to anyone. Nor was she
to know that it was the first of many times she was
to attempt an explanation, to her mother, to her
aunt, to herself ...

Because he did stay in Brisbane, in fact on and
off for over a year ...

'And that first meeting,' a seven-years-older
Hillary Morris whispered to herself in the
solitariness of her Paddington bedroom, after a
traumatic night, 'was probably the one and only
time I wasn't in love with him, secretly or
otherwise. Or thought I was. I may have been a
late starter but it didn't stop me from ... Oh hell!'
A tear slid down her cheek as she couldn't help
thinking of that younger version of herself.

He had left the hotel without seeing her again
after his last concert. She hadn't really expected to
see him, but there had been a lurking disappoint-
ment all the same. She had tried to get a ticket for
one of his remaining concerts but they had been
fully booked, so she had bought one of his records

instead, and it was only when she got it home that she had discovered a full cover picture of him on the back. A curious picture perhaps for a classsical recording, but whoever had set it up had known what they were about. He wasn't in evening clothes but in his shirt sleeves and with his tie loosened and his hands shoved into his trouser pockets as he leant against a wall. And he wasn't looking at the camera but with a brooding sombreness, and an almost tangible air of dislike, at a violin lying on a table.

And Hillary had caught her breath and felt a curious sensation at the pit of her stomach, and found herself remembering what an old nun had said to him. It is like a love affair for him, she'd thought a little shakily.

And the recording had confirmed it for her, for that barely smothered tension had come through in bursts of savagery, to be swept aside in lovely, lilting melodies, sad gentleness and, sometimes, a piercing sweetness that took your breath away.

But why the knowledge of it affected her so deeply, she'd been unable to say . . .

Curiously, at about the same time, she had fallen out with her mother and been conscious of an inexplicable feeling of restlessness. It hadn't been a thing of so many words, the falling out she had experienced with her mother; more a lack of them if anything—as if some of their channels of communication had become clogged.

Bea Selby had noticed it, though, and reflected that it was probably long overdue. And she had talked to her sister Marlene and tried to persuade her to get herself some outside interests, anything that would break the almost stifling closeness her niece and her sister lived in. 'Look,' she'd said,

'Dad's left us both comfortably off. Don't you think it's time you started to live a little? How about coming to Hong Kong with me next month? The shopping's marvellous even if you can't find anything else to like about the place.'

'And leave Hillary?'

Precisely, Bea had muttered to herself. But the fact that she was not the only stubborn member of the family had entered her calculations and she'd said quite mildly, 'Hillary can look after herself for a month or so.'

'I couldn't do it!'

'She's eighteen. And she's been working for some time now. Do you go to work and hold her hand?' A slip, a slip, Bea had chided herself mentally. I was planning to be much more subtle . . .

'It's all very well for you to talk, Bea,' Marlene Morris had said just a little pathetically. 'But you've never had any children. You don't know what it's like.'

No, I don't, Bea had thought in a moment of sadness. And perhaps that's why I can see how important it is to let go of the strings, to talk in clichés. Only how to get it through to her?

But Hillary's mother had resisted all her efforts and in the end Bea Selby had given up.

Then her sister had called to see her one day in some agitation. 'Hillary . . . is acting rather strangely,' she'd said breathlessly. 'I think she has a boy-friend and I'm *sure* he's quite unsuitable, otherwise she'd be more open about it!'

But Bea had been in an impatient mood. 'Want to bet? When have you ever shown her that it's a perfectly natural, normal thing? Never, because you're still so wrapped up in the hurt of her father.

But be that as it may. Why don't you just ask her about it?'

'I ... Sometimes Hillary is just a little difficult to talk to these days,' Marlene had said defensively.

So it had been Bea who had spoken to her niece at the first opportunity. 'Your mother's a little worried about you, Hillary,' she'd said lightly. 'She thinks you have a boy-friend—not that there's anything wrong in that! But we'd like to meet him.'

And that had been the first intimation Bea had had that Hillary now had a mind of her own.

'I don't have a boy-friend, Aunt Bea,' she had said quietly.

'Well then, a friend?'

'I've got a few friends now.'

'No one special?' Bea had enquired with what she had hoped was the lightest touch, only to discover that to her ears it had sounded elephantine.

'Yes, but he's not a boy-friend.'

Bea had looked at her narrowly. 'In what way?'

But Hillary had smiled, her smoky-blue eyes as clear as the day. 'You don't have to worry, Aunt Bea.'

'All the same,' Bea had answered, honestly she suddenly realised, 'we do a bit ... For one thing, considering the tabs your mum keeps on you ...' she'd deepened her voice dramatically and pulled a comical face, 'how come you've managed to keep him to just a suspicious shadow?'

'Well, I get one afternoon a week off now that I'm working a later shift and sometimes I spend it with him. I ... I think he's a little bit at a loose end at the moment but,' Hillary had hesitated, 'if I tried to tell you about him, Aunt Bea, you wouldn't understand. Neither would Mum, but he only ever treats me like Grandfather did, so there's no need to worry. Besides, I'm nearly nineteen now.'

Bea had looked into Hillary's eyes and sensed an implacability about her which had given her cause to wonder where they had all inherited their stubbornness from, she and her sister and now her niece, and she had backed off and advised her sister to do the same. All the same, she had suddenly found herself understanding a bit of how her sister felt.

'And I,' Hillary murmured to herself the morning after the ball as she smoothed the sheet restlessly, 'went blithely on, seeing Clive. I was so surprised when I got that phone call at work about three weeks after he'd left the hotel. But I didn't really stop to think. I accepted his offer to have a picnic lunch with him in the Botanic Gardens because it was my afternoon off. I can still remember the egg and cucumber sandwiches he brought . . . I can still remember it all so well . . .

In fact they spent nearly the entire afternoon in the Gardens, soaking up the clear winter sunshine.

And it was the first of their unusual outings which so enchanted her. Sometimes they went across the river to the Art Gallery where you could sit outside after you'd seen the latest exhibition and watch the seemingly peaceful Brisbane River flow by, with the city just across from you. Sometimes it was Newstead House, an historic early homestead of the city that sat on the confluence of Breakfast Creek and the main river, and fascinated Hillary not only for its lovely gardens and situation but for its restored interior. Or they went to New Farm Park; sometimes to King George Square outside the City Hall just to watch the world go by; if the weather was bad, to a film matinée, and once he showed her all his childhood haunts.

And all the time, she was falling more and more in love with him, although he did treat her very much as her grandfather had.

Only he wasn't her grandfather, of course. He was the stuff dreams were made of for Hillary. It was as if the veils of her mind were finally, belatedly, being lifted. But for all that it was a late awakening, it was more intense than anything that had ever happened to her.

Yet it wasn't only a physical thing. In fact it frightened her a little to think of his tall, well-made body and his long, strong hands. But she loved his smile and the way his grey eyes smiled sometimes too, and teased her. And she loved talking to him and the things they did which made her feel easy and comfortable.

But of course all this was her secret, this quite hopeless, star-struck feeling that left her breathless and happy beyond belief sometimes, or hauntingly sad at others. No one knew, not her mother nor her aunt, and least of all Clive, she hoped.

He told her that he had taken a flat in St Lucia, near the University of Queensland and not far from her home at Indooroopilly. And he told her that he might be staying longer in Brisbane than he had anticipated because Ned had arranged a tour of New Zealand for him in a month's time and was negotiating a concert series in Perth—on the other side of the continent.

'Senseless to go back to Europe in the meantime, isn't it?' he said, with a quizzical little smile.

And he told her that he'd visited his relations in Mackay—and not got much satisfaction from it, she'd sensed. He also told her that the Conservatorium of Music had asked him to consider a teaching seminar.

'Will you?' she asked.

'I'm ... considering it. The trouble is, I'm a lousy teacher. I don't have the patience.'

'I think you do.'

'You don't really know me, sweet Hillary. Or put it this way, you seem to bring out the best in me ...'

She hugged his words to herself that night in bed as if they were more precious than diamonds, and repeated them over and over to herself. And her happiness was pure and simple and quite undemanding.

Not long after that, though, things were no longer so simple. Because she quite unwittingly gave her secret away. At least, it happened accidentally. They were at Mount Coot-tha to take in the view of Brisbane and Moreton Bay and have a traditional Devon tea in the kiosk—it had been one of her grandfather's favourite spots.

But it was a very cold day for Brisbane, and Hillary shivered a little as they walked amongst the trees after their tea. And Clive quite naturally put an arm around her and pulled her close. 'It's a bit freezer's bold up here, isn't it?'

'Mmm ...' Her teeth chattered.

He laughed and kissed the tip of her nose. 'You're going blue,' he said, and put his other arm around her.

And that was when the world stopped for Hillary. She forgot how cold it was, and was only able to gaze up at him with her heartbeat tripping in a curious way and her lips parted.

'What is it?' he asked. 'You look as if you've seen a ghost!'

She blinked and wanted to move, but it was as if her feet were planted in the ground and she found herself remembering the only other time she had been in his arms, the day they had first met, and how supremely comforting it had felt—for that matter how it felt now, as if she never wanted to be anywhere else.

But unfortunately, all this was clearly visible on her face, she realised, as soon as she saw Clive's expression begin to change, to sober. And she bit her lip and started to blush furiously and wished she could die on the spot.

What happened, though, was that he let her go abruptly, and they walked to his car in silence.

A silence that lasted all the way along the tortuous road down Mount Coot-tha, a silence as painful for Hillary as Clive's change of mood.

Then he said, 'Hillary, I haven't been very wise, I'm afraid.' He put out a hand to take one of hers into it. 'But I'm not the right man for you.'

She swallowed miserably and for a moment pride tempted her to say something like, I never thought you were. Instead, cruelly, a strange feeling of desolation mixed itself up with her awful embarrassment, and a solitary tear splashed on to her cheek, then more and more.

'Oh hell,' he said softly, and pulled the car up. And he took her into his arms again and, as she'd done once before, she wept into his shirt. Only this time, after a little while, he tilted her chin up and kissed her lips very gently. 'Hillary, it could never be. It would be madness.'

'I know. I never thought . . .' she stammered. 'I mean, I never expected— But we could still be friends, couldn't we?'

'I think it's probably best if we weren't,' he said after a moment. 'You . . . should be going out with boys of your own age.'

She winced perceptibly.

'What's wrong with that?' His grey eyes probed her smoky-blue ones sombrely.

'I don't know any, for one thing.' Hillary made a desperate attempt to smile.

He smoothed her hair. 'How come? You know I've wondered about that. You seem to be a very solitary little person.'

'I guess I'm just shy.'

'Yes, I guess you are, and very sweet, but amongst other things I'm almost old enough to be your father and I'd make a terrible husband. Ask anyone,' he said with his lips quirking. 'Besides . . .'

'I know,' she said tremulously. 'I'm . . . just someone who's helped you to pass the time these last weeks, when you've been at a loose end.'

'Hillary, it's been more than that. I've enjoyed your company so much. And I'd give anything for this not to have happened.'

'Oh, it's all right. And I *didn't* ever think it would come to anything. But perhaps you're right . . . Anyway, you're going to New Zealand soon, aren't you?'

'Yes . . . Yes.'

'So—we could make this goodbye, then? Couldn't we?'

'Hillary . . .'

But she whispered then, 'Please don't say any more. I feel an awful fool. Oh, look, there's a bus coming I can catch that will take me nearly home. *Please!*'

Only there'd been an awful surprise waiting for her at home . . .

CHAPTER THREE

EVEN now, seven years later, Hillary couldn't help shivering and remembering with the utmost clarity her mother's contorted face and the things she'd said that cold afternoon . . .

'. . . Nothing but a cheap little tart. Oh, I always knew you'd turn out like your father! But with a man like that . . . How could you? Haven't you seen pictures of him in the women's magazines always with a different girl . . .'

'How did you k-know?' Hillary had stammered, white to her lips.

'Because I made it my business to find out. You've been out with him this afternoon, haven't you? Where? To his flat? Did he make love to you?'

'No! No . . . you don't understand . . .'

But nothing she'd said had halted the ugly tide of words that had spewed from her mother's mouth so uncharacteristically, and she'd finally run upstairs to her bedroom, crying and covering her ears, and she'd locked herself in and cowered beside her bed, shaking and weeping until finally she'd fallen asleep on the carpet exhausted.

It had been her Aunt Bea who'd tried to restore relations between her and her mother, her Aunt Bea who had tried to explain to her why her mother was the way she was . . .

'But how could she have said things like that to me if she loves me so much?'

'Out of concern, out of fear . . . Unfortunately,

49

Hillary, she has no one else and she's made you the very centre of her life . But I have to confess that most mothers would have been worried about you . . . seeing someone like Clive Eastman. He's— well, a lot older than you and you're very lovely,' Bea Selby had said.

To her surprise, Hillary had smiled, a bleak little smile. 'He doesn't think of me that way. He never did. I told *you* the truth about him, Aunt Bea, but you didn't understand any more than she does. He never tried to make love to me. We were just friends. Only now you've made it seem dirty and underhand . . . But you won't have to worry any more,' she had added with a sudden defiance. 'It's finished anyway.'

'Oh? Why?'

'Why?' Hillary had turned a strangely contemptuous glance on her aunt. Then her eyes had filled with tears and she'd said, 'Because he's going to New Zealand soon. And because, despite what you all think of him, he told me himself that he was too old for me and that I should make friends with boys of my own age. And I don't want to talk about it ever again.'

For a while it had been hard to talk to her mother, to forgive her for the things she had said. And for the first time in her life, Hillary had found herself thinking about her father, really thinking and wondering what he'd been like. And if he hadn't been perhaps as misunderstood as she had been . . .

But she had noticed gradually, as they'd moved like two strangers around her grandfather's house, how old her mother looked suddenly. As if that vicious outburst had aged her unbelievably. And how undecided she had become, and vague. And

one day it had been too much for her and she had
said over breakfast, which her mother always got
up and cooked for her, 'Oh Mum, I love you. I
always will.'

Her mother had lifted a pale, papery face, then
started to cry tears of relief. 'I'm so sorry . . .'

Yet, although they made their peace, Hillary
had been conscious from that point in time on, of
a strange burden. Only not even she had seen how
heavy it would become.

But two months later when she had run into
Clive Eastman accidentally, he had seen it
somehow and had felt it sufficiently to turn aside
his first instinct which had told him to ignore her.

In fact, she hadn't seen him striding across King
George Square. She had been busy feeding the
remains of her packed lunch to the pigeons. Then
she had got up and looked around once and
blinked and stood for a moment with her chin in
her hand as if she was old and recalling something
a long time ago.

And that was when he had called her name
involuntarily and she had jumped and looked
around.

'Oh,' she'd said. 'Oh, it's you.'

'Yes. How are you?'

'Fine! I'm fine. How was New Zealand?'

'What's wrong?'

'Nothing!' Hillary had licked her lips. 'I have to
get back to work.'

'I'll walk with you. Still working at the hotel?'

'Yes.'

'How is Mr Luigi?'

'Oh, we have a new manager now—Mr
Weisenbaum.'

'What's he like?'

She'd hesitated. 'Not as ... Not quite like Mr Luigi.'

Clive had laughed. 'Your loss,' he'd said. 'Mr Luigi was a genius. He even managed to calm me down one night. I quite remember threatening to throw him over the balcony, but he just stood his ground and said, please don't ... I haven't got a head for heights. Hillary, you look different. Why, I wonder ...?'

'You don't,' she had said, then flushed.

'Have you ... done what I suggested? Met some boys of your own age?'

'Yes, dozens! You were right, it's what I should have done ages ago.'

By this time they had arrived at the hotel concourse.

'Dozens?' Clive had lifted an eyebrow.

'No, not really, but some. I must run now. Goodbye—it's been nice to see you again.' And she had disappeared into the lobby.

Clive Eastman had stared after her for a time, and it had occurred to him that he'd thought a lot about her over the past two months, and that he'd missed her quiet, undemanding company more than he had thought possible. But he'd set his teeth then, and reminded himself that only a cad would take advantage of an adolescent crush. And he had spent that night with a lady who by no stretch of the imagination could have been described as adolescent.

Curiously, however, he had woken in a black mood the next day and rather summarily got rid of his lady friend and had fully intended to spend the day with his violin. But before he had left his flat for the Conservatorium of Music he had received a visit from a well-dressed, middle-aged woman who had almost shocked him into speechlessness with what she had come to say to him.

It was Hillary's mother. She had read, she'd said, that he was back in town, that he would be holding a special seminar at the Conservatorium and that he would also be doing a series of concerts for the Australian Broadcasting Corporation, for television. She had then gone on to demand that he stay away from her daughter during this time, and she had called him some rather ugly names . . . a seducer of innocent young girls being one.

Clive had heard her out in silence, mainly because of the sheer unexpectedness of it all. But by the time she had finished, he'd found himself in the grip of a cold, terrible rage, although the only indication of it was the slight narrowing of his eyes. And if Marlene Morris had had the benefit of Ned Cartwright's wisdom which had come from years of association with Clive Eastman, she might have quailed in her elegant leather shoes. But she had never even heard of Ned, nor heard him say— which he had, not infrequently—when Clive rants and raves you have no worries: when he goes quiet that's when you know you've got trouble, that's when you really find out what a difficult, dangerous bastard he can be . . .

But all Hillary's mother had observed was that he had gone a little pale. And all he had said was, 'You've made a mistake, Mrs Morris. If you've nothing left to say, I'll see you out.'

And the rest is history, thought Hillary, coming back to the present. Knowing Clive as I do now, I can quite believe that he then set out to seduce me, but for that matter he told me so anyway—later.

Told me that he'd then discovered he had some scruples he hadn't known he possessed and that's why he'd married me first . . . But it was doomed from the start for so many reasons. My mother . . . But I can't blame her entirely.

She stared up at the ceiling and found her eyes wet with tears as she thought of the sick, pathetic creature her mother had become after their marriage. And the series of heart problems she had had which had meant that for months Hillary had had to spend more time, almost, with her than with Clive. And she thought of how torn she had felt between the two of them—two irreconcilable enemies. And how she had once tried to explain to Clive that they had each other but her mother had no one, not even her Aunt Bea, who had gone to live in Greece for that summer.

'Hillary,' he had said to her harshly, 'she's got to learn some time to give you up. If she'd had her way she'd have kept you a spinster for the rest of her life.'

'I know . . . that,' Hillary had whispered. 'When she's well again . . .'

But there had been other pressures on Hillary, pressures that had eaten away at the sheer delight of her marriage—and it had been like an enchanted world for her those first early months when Clive had taken her to his bed and she had lain beside him in the moonlight, sometimes the sunlight, and he had loved her until it was as if she could feel the blood beating through her body in a sweet tide she had never guessed at through all those months of being in love with him.

And he had laughed at her sometimes and teased her gently. 'Who would have guessed that underneath that lovely but so prim exterior, there'd be such a passionate little girl?'

'Do you mind?'

He had studied her porcelain-pale body beside him, her small, pink-tipped breasts, her eyes that couldn't disguise how she felt about him, and then he had pulled her into his arms and said huskily, 'Of course not. Don't ever change, sweet Hillary.'

Nor did I, in that way, she mused. But things went wrong all the same. Not only because I just couldn't abandon my mother, although I'd let Clive persuade me to marry him in spite of all her threats and tantrums and so on ... But also because he was often impossible—moody, so tense; impossible to live with even for me, who adored him, or thought I did. Perhaps I should have stood up to him more? But I just wasn't made that way—then. I used to shrivel up inside and go quiet and stiff and try to pretend I didn't mind the things he sometimes said, the way he could be so impatient, only I minded so much I felt like dying sometimes. Perhaps I should have been like Ned—who I never got to meet, but I did know his philosophy. Perhaps I should have borrowed it and let it all run off my back like water off a duck's, and put it down to the artistic temperament.

Then there was the circle of people we moved in, so sophisticated whereas I was so naïve and shy. It became a form of torture for me and I began to want to shut myself into the flat and not go out. In fact that was one of my few sources of consolation, the flat and the fact that Clive gave me *carte blanche* to decorate it. It was my only haven, other than his arms ... And I used to get so tired, tired from trying to keep up with him, his friends, from worrying about my mother, worrying about how I was failing as a wife, as a companion . . . so tired.

'But the crisis came,' she murmured aloud to herself, 'when he decided to go back overseas. I knew he had to, that it had to come, that there was no way I could expect him to stay in Australia. I also knew it would be for a long time. I just didn't know how I was going to leave my mother. So I suggested following him in a couple of months, when she was well again . . .' She closed her eyes and what had followed came back to her as vividly as the day it had happened.

'. . . Hillary, so long as you're married to me, your mother will never be well again. Don't you understand that?'

'I . . . I . . .'

'It's the truth, Hillary,' he had said tersely, his grey eyes dark and angry. 'So come with me now, or not at all.'

She had stared at him, her face paling, not wanting to believe what she was hearing yet with one part of her expecting it, for the last few months had not been easy. In fact when they hadn't been making love, life had been hell, put quite simply.

She had licked her lips and tried to speak several times and had only been able to say finally, 'Clive . . . I . . . Clive, I can't leave her just now, don't you see?'

He had turned away from her abruptly and when he had turned back there had been something in his eyes that had frightened her. 'Yes, I see,' he had said unemotionally. 'And I think perhaps the time has come for you to see and to understand. Hillary, I'm not proud of this, but your mother threw down the gauntlet to me once and I picked it up. In a fit of rage and ... madness, I picked it up.' And he had gone on to tell her about his first meeting with her mother, something which, for reasons of their own, neither of them had ever mentioned to her before . . .

'So . . . that's why you married me,' she'd said through a curious obstruction in her throat. 'Do you mean, if she hadn't accused you of those things, you wouldn't have?'

'No, I wouldn't have.'

'Oh . . .'

'Hillary, look, it's not that I don't love you . . . in a way, but I knew you were too young and unworldly for me, I knew I'd make a lousy husband for you and I'd made up my mind never to see you again. I knew it was insanity to . . . that I'd be everything your mother said I was if I took advantage of what you felt. But when she said those things I—well, I have a reputation for being insane sometimes. Only I've never before regretted my moments of insanity quite as much now, and I think we have to end this thing *now* before you get hurt any more.'

'What do you mean?' she faltered.

'That we get a divorce. It's never going to work, Hillary. For that matter, it hasn't been working for some time now, has it?' he had added, and his grey eyes had probed hers mercilessly.

And perhaps, through over-tiredness, over-strain, whatever, for the first time in my life, I stood up for myself, thought Hillary, as she remembered what she had said then with her mind reeling and a sense of hurt in her heart almost too great to bear, 'How *could* you? How could anyone do a thing like that? And you're right, the last thing I want to do is stay married to you. I'll go now.'

'Where?'

'Home.'

'Hillary, don't go home. Find yourself a place of your own at least. You won't have to worry about money. But to go home is playing right into your mother's hands.'

'You can talk,' she'd said thickly.

'Yes, I can,' Clive had retorted. 'I may be a bastard, but anyone could see what your mother's doing to you.'

But she had started to cry then. 'I hate you, Clive! It's all right for you to walk out on me, to marry me in a fit of anger, to ... to ... But just don't think you can dictate to me any more. I've had enough of that, and you, and I'll go where I want. I'm sorry I've been such a bore to you and so young for you—you should have told me sooner instead of letting me go on making a fool of myself. I'm surprised you haven't found yourself a mistress, someone more elusive than I was, and wayward and ...' She'd stopped. 'Have you?' she'd whispered.

They'd stared at each other for an age. Then Clive had said, 'Yes ...'

'Now I really hate you,' she'd said, and her eyes had burned with it and it was as if her whole body was consumed with it.

'I'm glad.'

'Glad?' She had stared at him, stunned.

'Because I'd rather you hated me than blamed yourself. And you never made a fool of yourself, believe me.'

'I'll never believe another word you say. Goodbye, Clive.'

'Hillary ...' He'd put out a hand, but she'd

turned and run from the room.

Not only from the room, she mused, but I ran out of his flat and his life. She sighed suddenly and pleated her broderie anglaise pillow slip. And I went home to my mother who was triumphant and frequently reminded me that she'd told me so, and a lot more about men, besides. And I nursed her through all her ailments, imaginary or otherwise, until she died, not of her heart problems but while she was crossing the street at the same time as a drunken maniac was loose in his car. And all the time, apart from once when Aunt Bea came home and I broke down and told her the whole story, brick by brick I built up a wall in my mind around the memory of Clive, until I could even read about him and not care.

'So why did I make a scene like that last night?'

Her words seemed to echo oddly around the bedroom. Then the phone beside her bed rang and it was Ray.

'I'm fine,' she said into it. 'Actually I'm still in bed, but it is Saturday and Wendy's handling the shop—better than I do, I sometimes think,' she added with a grimace. 'It's also twelve o'clock closing today . . .'

She listened for a while, then she said, 'Ray, not today. I feel rather as if I've been under a steamroller. I think I'll just rest. Besides, I think you ought to see your father. We've . . . You've got to straighten some things out with him. So how about tomorrow?'

She put the phone down a little later and stared at her hands for a while and at the diamond ring she now wore. Then she pushed the bedclothes aside and got up to take a shower.

*   *   *

'It's been a great morning, Hillary,' Wendy Fenton said to her enthusiastically, as Hillary helped her to shut up shop. 'I even sold that perfectly ugly—in my opinion anyway—bamboo planter, not to mention . . .'

She had worked for Hillary for the past two years after a chance reunion during which she had told Hillary how she had left the hotel after several years of trying and failing to get on with Mr Weisenbaum, of being overseas on a protracted working holiday, and how she was now at a loose end.

'Are you still . . .?' she had asked Hillary awkwardly.

'No. Divorced.'

'I'm sorry, so sorry. Talk about shorn lambs and the slaughter, was I ever right,' Wendy had added obscurely, and never mentioned it again. And since then they had made a perfect team, for Wendy's strong points were Hillary's weakest, like accounts and badgering errant suppliers when they had an interior decorating job on, and they had become firm friends as well.

'How was last night?' asked Wendy, then she caught sight of the diamond engagement ring. 'Oh! I suspected this might happen. Congratulations! I like Ray,' she added sincerely.

Hillary looked at her a little wryly. 'I'm glad someone approves.'

'Who doesn't?' Wendy demanded.

'My aunt, for one. She thinks he's as dull as ditch water. Nor does his father approve of me any more, unfortunately.'

'Why ever not?'

'Wendy, you won't believe what happened last night.'

'Try me.'

'Clive turned up. And, as only he could do it—well, let's just say I've never been more embarrassed in my life.'

Just as Irene Saunders had the night before, Wendy too did a double-take, but in the act of closing the cash register. 'He didn't,' she said feebly. 'But why?'

'I haven't the faintest idea,' Hillary said wearily. 'And that's why Charles Saunders no longer thinks I'm quite eminently suitable for his son.' She told Wendy briefly what had occurred.

'Oh, but that's ridiculous!' Wendy said scornfully. 'I mean, you were respectably married to the man, and respectably divorced. It wasn't as if . . .' She stopped.

'Actually, I'm probably the only person—woman—who has ever been respectably associated with Clive,' Hillary said drily. 'Only it seems there've been so many others—women—I've sort of . . . been tarred with the same brush. At least I presume that's how Charles Saunders sees it. You must admit Clive has been—well, very open about his affairs.'

'Hillary,' Wendy said straightly, 'believe me, I hold no brief for Clive Eastman. In fact, for what he did to you I could quite easily take to him with a sharp knife when I think of how . . . well, how you were then. But Charles Saunders,' she said deliberately, 'is the last person who should be pointing a finger. I *know*. The only difference is, he conducts his affairs clandestinely—actually there's another difference: at least Clive Eastman is not married now and cheating on his wife.'

Hillary stared at her, her eyes wide.

'I worked in hotels and motels for twenty years, Hillary,' Wendy said softly. 'I saw it once with my own eyes. You'd be amazed at what I've seen, actually. And word gets round too. Not that I normally spill these kind of secrets; I figured it was none of my business anyway. Now I think it is. He's in no position to be thumbing his nose at you, Hillary. Not even *if* you'd lived in sin with Clive Eastman.'

'But I could never tell Ray that,' Hillary said huskily, her eyes still shocked.

'He might know it.'

'I don't think so . . .'

'What are you going to do, then?' asked Wendy.

'I . . . I don't know. I suppose I'm hoping it will all just blow over. And wishing,' Hillary added honestly, 'that Ray had a different father. I never really liked him. But I suppose no one knows better than I what a tricky thing parents and parents-in-law can be.'

That afternoon Hillary pottered around her cottage, a thing she normally didn't get much time for but always found soothing and relaxing.

It was small and apart from the connecting door into the shop, it had another private entrance at the side through a patch of garden; at least it had originally been a patch of tired grass, but Hillary had paved most of it and converted it into a courtyard with lots of potted shrubs and scented plants. And from the original, lead-light fan-shaped window above the side door, it was lovingly furnished, with antiques for the most part, all rich in texture and colour and shown up uniquely by the beautiful honey-coloured cedar walls in which the whole house was panelled. But her passion for antiques and textures and colours hadn't led her to clutter the place up and every

lovely piece she owned made its own statement.
Like the deep blue and clear greens of the Chinese
carpet in the lounge, which she had bought from
an old lady who had lived in Macau and been
obliged to part with her most treasured possession
because of an unquenchable thirst, probably
acquired in Macau too, for gambling. And there
were the lovely lines of the restored bentwood
dining-room chairs that stood around an English
oak gate-legged table in a corner of the lounge. In
the kitchen, the red stone tiles on the floor
provided a perfect foil for the wooden cupboards
and the copperware. And in the bedroom was a
wide four-poster bed with delicate cream hangings.

And from the veranda that ran right round the
back part of the cottage, indeed from all the main
rooms which opened on to it, she had a lovely
view down to the city.

Only on that Saturday afternoon, she found that
the dusting and polishing she did, didn't soothe
her particularly, and she gave it up and, on an
impulse, lay down in a patch of sunlight on the
Chinese carpet to listen to music on FM radio,
only to fall deeply asleep.

What woke her, she didn't know. She just
opened her eyes suddenly with a curious feeling of
expectancy and after a moment pushed herself up
on her arms to a half-sitting position, and turned
her head slightly—to freeze.

For Clive Eastman was standing in the french
windows, witness to the fact that she was half-
lying on the carpet with her legs and feet bare, her
loose blue caftan pushed up to her slender thighs,
her hair falling in her face which was flushed from
sleep, and her mind dazed and uncomprehending.

'Hillary,' he said, when she closed her eyes

experimentally to test, although he didn't know it, whether he was still part of her dream, 'sorry, but I knocked and I thought you must be here although there was no answer because I could hear the radio. So I came round.'

Hillary sat up properly and pulled her dress down. She took the slide out of her hair and opened it with her teeth and gathered the strands which had escaped it back into place—she did it all quite slowly to cover the erratic beating of her heart and because her voice wouldn't be steady, she knew.

Then she stood up lithely. 'What do you want?' she said finally and coldly. 'You frightened the life out of me!'

'I'm sorry,' he said again, and stepped into the room. 'You made a lovely picture, asleep like that,' he added with a slight smile.

She set her teeth. 'You've got an incredible nerve, Clive,' she said softly and bitterly.

He lifted an eyebrow. 'Not happy to see me, Hillary?'

'Did you really think I would be? You were . . . Last night, you were . . .'

'I know,' he interrupted. 'I came to apologise.'

Hillary stared at him for a moment with her lips parted and her eyes stormy and contemptuous. Then she took a deep breath. 'All right. And now you've done it you can go.'

'I also came to talk to you,' he said mildly.

'We have nothing to talk about.'

'Oh, I think we do. Why don't you offer me a cup of tea?'

'A cup of . . . Get out!' she gritted through her teeth.

'I'm afraid you're going to have to throw me

out,' Clive replied, with his grey eyes glinting wickedly.

For a moment she was really tempted to try, angry enough at least to feel like slapping his face, anything—for more reasons than one, she realised with an inward shiver. Because he hadn't changed much, and that brought back a host of old memories and hurts which she was so sure she'd forgotten. Because she'd been dreaming of him. Because . . .

She turned away abruptly and bit her lip—and thought, oh no, he can't do this to me. I've grown up, among other things. And I know just how to treat him now.

'Well,' she said, turning back, 'what's a cup of tea between . . . exes? Only don't count on staying too long afterwards, will you?' she added politely. 'I'd have no qualms about calling the police. Still strong, white and no sugar?'

'I'm surprised to hear you admit you remember that,' Clive said ironically, and followed her into the kitchen.

'I've always had an excellent memory,' she murmured, as she switched on the kettle. 'That might be one reason why I took such exception to what you did and said last night. For that matter, why I find it curious, to say the least, that you should want to talk to me now. From my point of view, you said it all in a few short sentences about six years ago. Still, we live and learn.'

'My, my,' he marvelled, 'you have changed! Six years ago you were never so articulate.'

'No, I wasn't, was I?' she agreed, as she poured boiling water on to the teabags. 'But I've done a lot of growing up since then,' she added levelly, and put two mugs down on the counter between

them. 'Pull out a stool,' she invited, and got out
the milk and sugar. 'We'll have it in here.' She sat
down herself. 'Yes—enough to know that you
were right, it could never have worked for us. And
that my mother was a lot to blame for what
happened,' she added very quietly, stirring her tea
and staring down at it.

'Hillary . . .'

'No, let me finish, Clive. I also came to
understand,' she raised her eyes suddenly, 'although not at the time, that what you did was
the best way out of it. To have dragged on for
years would have been the final insanity. I
understand that now and can even be grateful.
Which is what you wanted, I think. Wasn't it?'
There was something very direct and challenging
in her eyes.

'Yes,' he said, but on an oddly dry note.

'Then why, now that I've made a new life for
myself, and found someone who really loves me,
did you throw a spanner in the works like that last
night?'

His eyes narrowed faintly. 'I wasn't to know he
really loves you.'

'Well he does.'

'Then nothing I did should alter that. But since
you ask, I'll tell you what happened last night. It's
what I wanted to explain anyway. I had no idea I
was going to see you, and I suppose it was only
because there were so many people there that I
didn't see you earlier. Then that spotlight came on
and you were in it, to my . . . intense surprise let's
say, and on top of that, well I told you what I
thought of the whole production. I have an inbuilt
aversion to the political bandwagon bit, I guess,
because I've seen a lot of it, and seen how fake it

can be. And upon reflection, I suddenly found myself thinking that it wasn't what I wanted for you.'

'But . . .'

'Hang on, it's my turn now. That was my first reaction and I guess that's why I came up to make myself known.' He grimaced. 'Not very diplomatic, I agree, but then I've never been famed for my diplomacy. What happened next was the bit I really regret,' he said. 'But it seems there's always been something about you, Hillary, that brings out the worst in me.'

'You told me once . . . You . . .' She bit her lip.

'The way things turned out though, have proved the opposite, haven't they?' he said curtly.

She stood up suddenly and walked over to the window, to stand there staring out with her arms clasped about her.

'If I didn't know better,' she said huskily at last, 'I'd be tempted to think it's a case of, you don't want me yourself but you don't want anyone else to . . . have me.'

'That might be true . . .'

She swung round. 'Only it's not. I could have remarried any time in these last six years and you wouldn't even have known it—or whether I was dead or alive, for that matter.'

'And that upsets you?' he queried, his eyes curiously probing and sombre.

'No! Yes . . . of course it does in *this* context. You have no right, it's none of your business any more. *You* made that decision. So to walk back into my life now, and . . . and complicate it as you did—yes, it upsets me, and angers me, quite justifiably, I think.'

'And have you stopped to think how complicated your life could become soon? Charles Saunders . . .'

'I'm not marrying Charles Saunders, I'm marrying his son!'

'Then you didn't get the slightest intimation last night of the kind of influence and pressures Ray Saunders is subject to from his father?' Clive asked mockingly.

'I . . .' Hillary lifted her shoulders in a suddenly weary gesture, and sat down. 'Yes, I did. And not only last night. I'm not quite dumb, you know.'

'You don't mind, then?'

'I do mind. But, when you love someone, you have to be prepared to take on their problems as well, don't you?' she said very quietly.

He smiled. 'A fitting thrust at me, Hillary.'

'What do you mean?' She looked genuinely perplexed for a moment. 'Oh,' she said then, 'my mother. But there was a difference with us. You didn't . . .'

'I didn't really love you,' he finished for her. 'And now you *really* hate me, don't you?' he added softly.

She took her time. 'No. I told you, I understand now. I can even,' she smiled wryly, 'appreciate your concern, and if it's of any interest to you, you're not the only one . . .' She stopped abruptly and bit her lip. Why did I say that? she wondered.

'I know.'

She looked at him with a frown between her eyes. 'You know? How?'

Clive seemed to hesitate slightly. 'From what you used to tell me of your aunt, I couldn't help wondering if she approved.'

'Well,' she shrugged, 'she has some odd ideas, too. By the way, how did you find where I lived?'

'It wasn't that difficult. I peered into your shop and was . . . impressed.'

'Thank you!'

'Someone mentioned last night that you do interior decorating, too.'

'Yes.'

'As a matter of fact I've just bought a house that needs redecorating. I don't suppose you'd be interested.'

Hillary stared at him. 'You mean—you're going to live in Brisbane?' she asked incredulously.

He grinned. 'Don't look so shocked! I've . . . retired.'

'Why?'

'Who knows? I got tired of it.'

'What . . . what are you going to do?' she asked blankly.

'Oh, this and that. Settle down. My dear Hillary,' he laughed, 'if you could see your face! Is it so impossible, do you think?'

'Come and see me in six months' time,' she said drily, then took a steadying breath. 'Clive, I hope you don't mean to . . . go on . . . Well . . .'

'Complicating your life?' he supplied. 'I don't see why we can't be friends. You say you don't hate me, you're even grateful to me and we once were . . . good friends. I should imagine it would be a sign of maturity too.' He looked at her quizzically.

Hillary compressed her lips. Then she said as calmly as she was able, 'You know very well why . . . it's quite impossible.'

He stood up and came round the counter and, taking her by surprise, drew her to her feet. 'I know that some people would like to dictate that to you. Just as you'll find them dictating a whole lot else besides. But I've always found it's best to be your own man. Try it,' he advised, looking down at her enigmatically. Then he bent his head and kissed her lips and she stood like a stone statue, unable to move a muscle. 'That was for old times' sake, by the way, that's all. See you around, Hillary,' he said, and walked out of the back door.

Hillary put a hand to her mouth, then pulled it away as if she had burnt it. And she picked up one of the mugs from the counter and threw it violently against the wall. To stare distractedly at the bits of earthenware that landed at her feet. Then she dropped her head into her hands and started to cry angrily.

CHAPTER FOUR

'HILLARY, my dear,' Charles Saunders said expansively, 'sit down. I'm so very glad you allowed Ray to bring you along this afternoon. I'm afraid I have some explaining and apologising to do!' He winked jovially and ushered Hillary to a chair.

'How are you, dear?' said Irene Saunders, sitting down opposite her. 'What a miserable Sunday afternoon! And just when one quite thought that lovely autumn weather was going to last for ever.' She glanced ruefully out of the wide windows. It was pouring.

'Yes,' Hillary murmured, and found herself thinking that her mother-in-law to be didn't look well. She was beautifully groomed as always and her chartreuse velvet trouser suit was superbly cut, but the line of her shoulders beneath it looked too thin, and her eyes tired.

'Was it raining on your side of town?' Charles Saunders enquired politely, yet somehow contriving to make it sound as if Hillary's side of town was way down the scale compared to his. Which it was, she mused. For Ray's parents lived in Ascot, in one of the showpiece mansions the area boasted.

'Yes, it was!' she said a little ingenuously. It rains in Paddington, too, she felt like adding, but didn't.

'Well, I suggest we have a drink,' said Ray. 'To take off the chill. What will it be, Hillary? Mother?'

They both settled for a sherry.

'Now, Hillary,' Charles said with a grimace, 'Ray here really read me the riot act yesterday. And of course he was right for the most part. I did over-react on Friday night, and I did ... say some unforgivable things in the heat of the moment. Unfortunately, we do have a slightly ticklish problem with your ... former husband.' He shot a swift glance at Ray, but his son was staring into the flames of a log fire burning in the huge stone grate. 'Although, in a sense, I'm glad that I know *now* and not later.'

'I don't see what difference it makes,' Hillary said. 'Nothing can change it.'

Charles Saunders dipped his head in acknowledgment. 'But at least we can be prepared for it.'

'Prepared for what?'

'The day some vicious scandalmonger tries to use it against Ray—and believe me, my dear, when you're in the public spotlight as Ray is, and hopes to be more and more, there are plenty of people who try to do that!'

'Mr Saunders,' Hillary said evenly, 'the fact that I'm a divorcee is unalterable. I know it offends some people's religions, but then you always knew I was. And apart from that ... fact, there is no scandal to be dug up.'

'Oh, I believe you, Hillary! *I* do ...'

'When many people wouldn't,' she interrupted. 'Is that what you mean? Then I think you're still over-reacting, if you'll forgive me for saying so.'

Ray raised his head suddenly. 'Dad ...'

'Ray,' his father said placatingly, 'we did agree that I could try to explain it to Hillary.'

Ray opened his mouth, then glanced at his mother and shrugged. And for the first time since she'd known him, Hillary was suddenly aware of how deeply he cared for his mother.

'To have been associated with a man like that, however innocently, and I'm sure it had to be, you were so young.' Charles said delicately, 'places you in a rather vulnerable position, Hillary. People being people,' he said indulgently, 'some of them might think ... what kind of a person is she really?'

Hillary stared at him. 'He's not a rapist or a murderer, Mr Saunders! He's also a very highly-respected and famous musician. There are people, too, who would consider it an honour to know him. In fact he's a very famous Australian. I'm sorry, but I think this is ridiculous!'

'If you really cared for Ray, you might understand,' Charles Saunders shot at her. 'The man is a notorious womaniser, whatever else he is!'

'If he was half the womaniser he's made out to be,' Hillary said hotly, 'he'd be dead and buried by now. A lot of it is press speculation.'

'But not all of it,' he said softly. 'And you do admit then that some people are vulnerable to press speculation and that kind of thing?'

There was an uncomfortable silence.

'All right,' Hillary said finally, 'yes. But I still don't see how *I* could be.'

'Ah,' said Charles, suddenly radiating goodwill, 'with a bit of planning and foresight, perhaps you won't be. Er ... how's your sherry? Oh, just a sip left, I'll pour you another.'

Hillary surrendered her glass feeling as if she sorely needed another one.

Irene Saunders said softly, 'I'm afraid it's one of the penalties of being anyone political's wife ... you're expected to be like Caesar's wife.'

Hillary thought of what Wendy had told her about Charles Saunders and closed her eyes briefly. Why does she put up with it? she wondered. She must know, surely. Which means she must know what a pompous sham he is!

The answer to this came to her in a sudden flash of insight. For Ray's sake?

'Now the first thing we have to do,' Charles said boyishly—he's pulling out all stops, Hillary reflected grimly—'is get our stories to tally. You were very young and bedazzled, Hillary, by Clive Eastman, but you came to your senses quite soon—how long were you married, by the way?'

'Nine months—nearly two years if you count the twelve months' separation before the divorce.'

'Excellent! You came to your senses very soon. I wonder if there were grounds for an annulment? Not that we can do anything about that now. And of course *you* left him.'

Hillary was silent.

'Because he was unfaithful to you?' The words were softly spoken and insidious. Still she said nothing. 'In fact in the old days you could have got a divorce on the grounds of mental cruelty, too, probably?'

'Charles . . .' Irene spoke a little anxiously. 'Let's just leave it at that.'

'Very well. Are we agreed on this, Hillary?'

'Yes . . . No.'

'There's more?' Ray's father asked alertly.

'No. Only this. Why I married Clive and why I got divorced from him is nobody's business but mine. So if anyone wants to know about it, send them to me, Mr Saunders. I'll be able to tell them that, even if you can't.'

Ray moved at last and came to stand by her

chair. 'I agree with her,' he said.

For a moment it looked as if there would be an explosion of wrath similar to Friday night's. But he was better than that, Charles Saunders—better on Sunday afternoons than Fridays nights, at least, Hillary thought irreverently and also furiously. For he took control of himself and appeared to capitulate.

'So be it,' he said, and added, 'By the way, I like a woman of spirit! That could be a great asset to Ray. But there is one thing we do have to agree on, folks. You really can't have anything to do with the man now, Hillary.'

'I . . . Do you think . . .' Nine, ten, out . . . What does he *take* me for? 'Oh, I'm afraid I disagree there, too,' she said quite gently, considering her state of mind. 'As a matter of fact we're . . . underneath it all we're good friends mostly. I've even offered to redecorate his house. Did you know he's planning to settle in Brisbane? No? Well, it came as quite a surprise to me, too. But I do think it's much more . . . mature, to handle these things this way. Don't you honestly agree?' She set her sherry glass down with something of a snap. 'Ray,' she added, but a little faintly then, 'I think I ought to be going.'

'I'm sorry Hillary. He—my father,' Ray Saunders sighed suddenly, 'is so keen on my political career.'

The navy-blue Alfa Romeo pulled up at a traffic light and Hillary stared out at the deserted, rainswept street. 'I guess so,' she said dully.

'Were you serious about . . . redecorating his house?'

'At the time. Ray . . .' She turned her head.

'Hillary, I love you. And I trust you. I'm also

not quite as dumb as I sometimes appear. You've seen him again, haven't you?'

She stared into his blue eyes. 'Yes ... Not willingly. He came to see me to apologise, yesterday.'

'Are you ... good friends still?'

She closed her yes. 'No ...'

'Then you said that to make a stand against my father?'

'I'm sorry, but I find your father impossible to take sometimes.'

He laughed softly and drew her into his arms. 'So do I. He gets quite paranoid sometimes. I generally go along with him for my mother's sake. Hillary, do you have any regrets about Clive Eastman?'

'No, none.'

'Then do his house if you want to. Do it in a neo-colonial, neo-Nazi style if you like! I presume he must have asked you?'

'Yes, but ...?'

'Correct me if I'm wrong, but would you like to show him something, too?'

She caught her breath. 'What do you mean?'

He hesitated. 'That you're heartwhole and fancy-free of him for ever?' he said very quietly. 'I ... got the feeling on Friday night that he and my father might be ... two of a kind. Rather dictatorial people who need now and then to be taken down a peg or two ...'

'Oh Ray,' she whispered, her lips curving, 'I love you. I was so afraid ... I mean ...'

'I know. That I'd support my father. But the truth is, Hillary, where you're concerned, he hasn't got a leg to stand on.' And he bent his head to kiss her so thoroughly that it was quite some time before they realised there was a policeman knocking on his window.

'Look here, mate,' he said, trying not to grin, 'I know it's Sunday afternoon and there's not a lot of traffic, but you can't just sit here in the middle of the road doing this, you know. Even if the lady is gorgeous. There's a traffic by-law . . .'

'And that was my weekend, Aunt Bea,' Hillary said later that night. 'How was yours?'

'Nothing like as interesting as yours, my dear,' Bea Selby replied, still smiling to think of her niece's description of her recent contravention of the traffic by-laws.

'Interesting,' Hillary put her head on one side. 'If I wasn't so tired, I could think of a better word to describe it.'

'Then let's say Ray has . . . well, surprised me. A more *interesting* young man than I took him for, obviously.'

'I could have told you that.'

'And are you going to do it?'

'Do what?' Hillary was curled up in an armchair, wearing a smoky-blue dressing-gown that matched her eyes, and she and her aunt were partaking of hot cocoa. It was still pouring outside, but inside Hillary's house, with the lamps on and the curtains drawn, it was warm and snug. Only Hillary wasn't feeling altogether warm and snug inside. In fact, she reflected, she felt a little dangerously light-headed, as if she'd been mountain climbing or something equally strenuous. And in a way she had always had, it showed on her face. Her skin looked more translucent and her eyes were shadowed.

Her aunt had noticed this but said nothing.

Now she found herself regretting her question, though, and she said instead, 'Why don't you go to bed? You must be tired after so much trauma.'

'Because I don't think I'll sleep. Do what?'

'Redecorate his house,' said Bea with a sigh.

'Of course not.'

'It would be a . . . challenge.'

'The kind I could do without.' Hillary sipped her cocoa.

'But . . . well, I'm sure you're right,' Bea said peaceably. So uncharacteristically peaceably that Hillary set her cup down and eyed her aunt suspiciously. 'You don't think that at all, unless you've changed dramatically in the last forty-eight hours!'

'Hillary, do you want me to talk you into redecorating his house or out of it?

'Out of it! It's the last thing I want to do!'

'Then why did you ever mention it?'

'Because . . . because . . . oh *hell*! You should have heard me, Aunt Bea, defending Clive with my dying breath, almost. It was crazy, but Ray's father does that to me.'

'I think Clive deserved to be defended—oh, in a general sense. For that matter I've always had my doubts whether Charles Saunders is quite the pillar of society one has been led to believe.'

Hillary opened her mouth, then shut it again for reasons not quite clear to her.

'And to get back to the particular,' Bea went on, 'if Ray doesn't mind . . .'

'I think Ray was simply making a point. That he trusts me. Well, the point is taken, gratefully. I don't have to go out now and *prove* it.'

'Not even to yourself?'

'I don't know what you mean, Aunt Bea,'

Hillary said after a moment.

'I mean prove to yourself that Clive means nothing to you any more,' Bea murmured almost sleepily, but there was nothing sleepy in her eyes as they rested on her niece's downcast head.

'He doesn't . . . even if he might like to think he does.'

'Did he say that?'

'No, not in so many words. But,' Hillary hesitated, 'when I said something about . . . doing what he did out of a sort of dog in the manger attitude, he agreed.'

Bea smiled slightly. 'It would be funny if he wanted you back now, Hillary, wouldn't it?'

'Would it? Yes, it would be. Laughable.'

'You mean from your point of view?'

'And his. It's not that he wants me back. Only that his ego would like to think I'm . . . still in love with him.'

'That sounds very bitter and cynical, my dear.'

Hillary raised her head at last. 'Oh no. Just realistic.'

It was still raining four days later and everyone was bemoaning the fact that it was going to be a wet winter. Except Wendy Fenton, who tended to take a philosophical view of things. 'They'd be crying drought if it wasn't raining,' she said briskly that gloomy Thursday morning. 'They're never satisfied. Your,' she shot a piercing glance at Hillary over the pile of ledgers that lay on the table between them, 'er . . . personal life sorted itself out? Not that I'm prying . . .'

'I know,' Hillary said affectionately, and stretched. 'Actually, it's in a state of limbo at the moment. Ray's away down south at some tariff

conference and his father has either decided he's
flogging a dead horse or he's retired hurt for the
moment. I wonder why I suspect the latter?'

'Simple,' Wendy said shrewdly. 'Apart from
anything else, he won't take kindly to his only son
taking orders from someone else, so to speak. He's
not that kind of man.'

'I don't give Ray orders . . . but I know what
you mean,' Hillary said ruefully. 'So you think the
battle lines are being drawn up?'

'Wouldn't be surprised.'

'I thought—I really thought this kind of thing
only happened to eighteen-year-old kids! Ray's
thirty-four. Surely any self-respecting father would
understand that by that age you shouldn't still be
wanting to dominate your children?'

'You better believe it,' said Wendy. Then the
phone rang and when they resumed their
conversation it was about business. 'You going to
this sale, this afternoon?' Wendy held up a
newspaper cutting. 'House contents,' she read,
'featuring some . . . well, by the sound of it mainly
heavy old Victorian furniture.'

Hillary glanced at it and out of the window at
the teeming rain, then, in the act of saying no,
changed her mind. 'Yes, I think I will. I rather feel
like digging through boxes of old china. Who
knows what I might find? Yes,' she stood up, 'just
the kind of thing for a day like this. I feel lucky in
my bones. What time does the auction start?'

'Four. But it's open from two. Don't catch a
cold, will you?'

'I never catch cold,' Hillary said blithely, feeling
suddenly almost restored from the curious sense of
being over-burdened she had been experiencing all
week.

All the same, she dressed up warmly in a pair of jeans and high-heeled boots and a chunky scarlet jumper with a matching knitted hat and scarf and gloves. Scarlet suited her because of her very fair skin.

However, it was the house that entranced her more than the contents at first. At Bardon, not far from Paddington and not far from the the Governor's official Brisbane residence, it was in a quiet little back street and unusual in that it was a brick and plaster building, but very old. Yet it was solid. In fact the walls were about a foot thick and it had a lovely gable at the front over the long mullioned drawing-room windows, and the original kitchen and servants' quarters at the back were separated from the house by a covered walkway as had been the fashion a century or so ago. It also had a full quarter-acre garden which was about twice the size of the neighbouring gardens, a garden that had been neglected for a long time, by the look of the flowering creepers that had been let run amok, and the old fruit trees and the almost overgrown herb-garden. Not that Hillary had been able to inspect the garden closely because of the rain, but she had looked out at it from every window, and, on her way to the kitchen part, had stepped incautiously off the walkway and crushed a plant beneath her boot and immediately smelt thyme. So she had looked more closely and seen parsley and mint, chives and garlic growing right outside the kitchen door, virtually.

But her growing delight at the house had been tempered by two things—the furniture which was, as Wendy had predicted, mostly dark, heavy and overpoweringly ugly, and the feeling of fear almost in her heart, at what the fate of this old house was going to be. Demolition? she wondered. Were they going to build a block of shops here? Or run a road through?

And for a moment she was almost tempted to ask, but then she thought, what's the use? If they're going to do that, it's too late.

That was when she had made a discovery that proved her bones had been right, although she had begun to think that she was wasting her time. Either the owners of the house had had consistently bad taste or the best of the small stuff had been creamed off.

There were about a dozen cardboard cartons in the kitchen, mostly filled with junk. But one held the remanants of an old Spode dinner service, which she had fallen on with a cry of delight. For she herself had half of an identical dinner service but had given up hope of ever matching it up to make it complete. Yet in the carboard carton was every piece she was missing plus a few extras.

And she had bought it, being the only bidder, for a song, although she had had to wait almost to the end of the auction, as the kitchen contents had come under the hammer last. By which time the rain had got even heavier, if anything, and she was just contemplating how to get herself and her dinner service to her car with a hand free to hold her umbrella, when she looked up and saw Clive Eastman coming up the front steps.

'Why, Hillary,' he said, 'what are you doing here? Or can I guess?'

'Probably,' she said stiffly.

He looked into the box. 'Is that worth anything? I'd have thought not.'

'It will be, because I have the rest of it. Rather, I

have the rest of an identical one, and it was a limited edition. Not that I intend to sell it.' She frowned. 'What are you doing here? I didn't know you were interested in this type of thing. Besides, the auction's finished.'

'Well, I've always liked lovely things, but of course I'm not the expert you are—have become.' His eyes were amused. 'But it's a nice old place, isn't it?'

Hillary glanced around and found herself feeling curiously nettled. 'Nice?' she retorted. 'It's a gem! I'd give my eye teeth to own it. Now if your new home was something like this,' she added with a tinge of irony, 'I'd redecorate it like a shot. I wouldn't be able to resist it . . . What's so funny?'

'Well . . .'

But they were interrupted by the auctioneer coming out on to the veranda. 'Oh, Mr Eastman, not a terribly successful day, I'm afraid,' he said. 'And the weather hasn't helped. But according to your instructions, I let a lot of it go for a song just to get rid of it.'

Hillary's mouth fell open. 'You . . . you own it?' she whispered.

'Mmm.' Clive smiled at her. 'And I intend to live in it—after you've redecorated it, of course. You did say, not two minutes ago. . . '

'No!' she interrupted him hoarsely, her eyes furious. 'And would you mind getting out of my way!' He was still standing at the top of the steps.

'Not at all,' he said calmly. 'Here, I'll give you a hand.'

'I can manage,' she ground out, almost too angry with him, and herself, to speak. Unfortunately, it was as she was brushing past him, and clutching the box of crockery to her

bosom as if he would contaminate it by so much
as laying a finger on it, that she came to grief. She
slipped on the wet steps and with a cry of alarm
began to fall . . .

The next two minutes would have done justice
to a Laurel and Hardy movie as Hillary tried
desperately to save the dinner service, and Clive
and the auctioneer tried to save her. In the
confusion though, it was the box that was rescued
by the auctioneer with a spectacular sideways twist
of his body, and Hillary who evaded all their
efforts and ended up sitting on the path at the
bottom of the steps with one ankle doubled up
beneath her.

'Oh!' she breathed, and bit her lip.

'Hillary? Are you all right?' Clive was beside her
in the rain, lifting her up with his hands beneath
her armpits, staring down into her white face with
his eyes dark with concern.

'I'm fine. I . . .' she said shakily.

'No, you're not,' he answered roughly, and
picked her up.

'I am!' A note of something like hysteria entered
her voice, but he ignored it and carried her
upstairs and into the house.

'Here, put her here,' said the auctioneer,
anxiously fluttering around them and indicating an
over-stuffed settee. 'What we need is some
brandy!'

Clive put her down very gently and stood
looking down at her for a moment with a strangely
wry glint in his eyes. 'You haven't changed in
some ways,' he said softly. 'Still a little girl to hold
and to carry . . .'

Hillary closed her eyes and felt her cheeks begin
to burn.

But the next moment he was being strangely businesslike. 'What hurts most? Your ankle? Let's see . . .' And he knelt down and unzipped her boot and pulled it off carefully.

'I don't think it's broken or anything,' she said hastily. But he took his time about examining her stockinged foot, twisting it about in his hands. 'That hurt?' he asked, with an acute glance at her face.

'Not really,' she said ruefully. 'It just feels a little tender. It'll be fine.'

'Anything else hurt?' the auctioneer chimed in.

Hillary drew a deep breath and decided to try for a light note. 'Nothing hurts. I just feel—all shook up. No, seriously, I'm all right.'

'Then stay there for a minute and get your breath back,' said Clive, standing up. 'Bob and I have a few things to discuss, no doubt.'

Which she did, gratefully, while the two men discussed the auction. She laid her head back and deliberately willed herself to relax. What an idiot! she mused. In more ways than one. Then her mind went strangely blank as she lay back and listened to the two men talking about the arrangements that had been made with buyers for the removal of the heavy stuff still left in the house. But curiously, she didn't notice that their voices had faded, because she found suddenly that her mind was no longer blank, that it was as if a brick had been removed from the wall she had built around certain parts of her life, so that she could look again into that forbidden territory ... And see herself when she really had been a little girl struggling so desperately to keep up with a husband who was light years ahead of her in so many ways. Only there'd been one area of their lives, just one, which the differences between them had not, somehow, managed to contaminate. Clive had never been impatient with her in bed, not even when he must have been sleeping with someone else. Oh, sometimes he'd teased her, but he'd made her laugh, too. And sometimes he'd shocked her a little, because there was no part of her slender body he hadn't come to know intimately.

But most of all, perhaps, she had surprised herself because it seemed there was a side to her nature she had not really known existed. A side that had responded to his lovemaking more and more freely, something within that had made her tremble at a touch, at a look, and long to be in his arms. And when she was, it made her arch her body against the lean, hard length of him with a mixture of joy and yearning and a desire to please, and a capacity for pleasure herself that often left her unable to speak, only able to fall asleep within the the circle of his arms suddenly, like a child.

The thing is, she said to herself, as she turned her mind's eye forcefully away from those glimpses through the wall, was it ... was it because of a repressed girlhood that I ... blossomed so unbelievably? Was it *really* me, or a kind of hormonal over-reaction that circumstance and any man could have brought about? Or was it Clive? Because if it was him and only him, I'm in trouble ...

But why should I think that? she asked herself. It's years since I remembered. But that's just it, she argued with herself. Don't you know what did it, what broke through the wall? It was being held in his arms again. And the fact that you're afraid to be near him now, Hillary, aren't you?

'What are you thinking?'

Her eyes flew open and they stared at each other, grey eyes into smoky-blue ones.

'I . . .' She sat up. 'That I should be getting home. Where's . . . Has the auctioneer gone?'

'Yes. I'm going to lock up now.'

'Oh, definitely time to go home,' she said, and accepted his hand to stand up because it would have been churlish to refuse.

'I didn't mean that. But it's cold and gloomy in here now. Why don't you have dinner with me instead of going home?'

Hillary took a breath and tried to pull her fingers free, unsuccessfully. 'No . . . no, Clive,' she murmured looking down.

'Is your ankle still hurting?'

'No! I mean, not really. But I'm damp and a bit muddy and . . .' She stopped, conscious that she was floundering.

'Is it against the rules, then?' he said very quietly, and with his free hand tilted her chin so that she had to look at him.

'As a matter of fact it's *not*,' she said with an effort. 'At least, not anyone's but mine . . .'

Clive didn't say anything for a moment. Then, 'What were you thinking about just now? Tell me, was it about us, all those years ago?'

'No,' she whispered.

'It wasn't something . . . especially happy, though, was it?'

'I . . . No.'

'Then what other great unhappiness have you had, Hillary, to make you look like that?'

Her lips parted and, to her horror, tears welled in her eyes. 'Clive,' she began unsteadily, and stopped because the ground no longer seemed to be quite steady beneath her feet. Why? she wondered desperately, but knew the answer in her heart immediately. It was him, it was being so close to him, it was exactly what she'd feared. So some things haven't changed, she thought bitterly, and closed her eyes on her foolish tears. What had he often said? You don't come any higher than my heart. And in spite of everything, I'd still like to be there, in his arms, resting against his heart . . .

She turned away clumsily and because her ankle was still a bit sore, swayed uncertainly, and Clive put his arms around her from behind so that she was leaning back against him, crying.

'Hillary,' he muttered against her hair.

'Clive, don't do this to me,' she said in a voice clogged with tears.

'Then tell me why you're crying.'

But it seemed she couldn't, because she couldn't stop crying then. Not even when he led her outside to her car and put her into it. Nor when he searched through her bag and found her keys and got into the driver's seat. And barely when, after driving not very far, he pulled up outside a small restaurant.

'I *can't*,' she whispered then.

'Yes, you can. It's what you need. Here, borrow my hanky.'

The restaurant was small and dim but warm and cosy. It appeared that Clive knew the owner, who was also the chef, and he ushered them to a candlelit table behind a stand of plants that afforded some privacy—to Hillary's considerable relief. She was still clutching Clive's handkerchief.

But as she sank into the comfortable banquette, she was aware of a curious feeling of numbness and she laid her head back, no longer caring—about anything.

Food came speedily. A dish of golden cannelloni with a crisp side salad. And a bottle of Chianti. So she ate, and the cannelloni was delicious, and she sipped her wine and Clive made no small talk.

Then she found herself studying him openly as the dishes were removed and he declined dessert for them both. Studying his face, which was half-turned away from her, as he stared at nothing in particular, at the lines beside his mouth, his hand around the stem of his glass, the line of his shoulders beneath the jacket of a well-tailored navy-blue suit, his fair hair just touching the collar at the back, his autocratic profile that could look so forbidding in repose unless you knew how he could smile . . .

And it was as if she sighed a great sigh inwardly as she drained her wine and set the glass down.

And said, 'I'm still going to marry Ray Saunders.'

CHAPTER FIVE

FOR a moment there was no reaction, other than a barely perceptible tightening of Clive's fingers around the stem of his glass. He turned his head, but not to look at Hillary immediately. He refilled her wine glass and only then lifted his eyes to hers.

'I wonder if you ought to do that to him,' he said drily.

She sipped her wine and wondered instead why she should feel so calm, as if she had got rid of a vast burden, as if she was at peace again. And she wondered if it showed in her face, this new sense of serenity.

'Hillary?' There was a flicker of the old impatience in Clive's voice, but it only made her smile slightly.

'Do what to him?' she asked steadily.

'I think you must know what I mean. It seems there are some things that are not quite over—between us.' He shot her a rapier-like glance.

But she didn't even flinch. 'Yes, they are.'

'Then what got to you just now so ... deeply? Or are you going to pretend it didn't happen?' he asked scornfully.

Go on being like that, Clive, she said to him in her mind. It really helps. Not that I need help any more. The thing is, how to explain that to you?

'No,' she murmured thoughtfully, 'I'm not going to do that. I suppose there are some things it's quite natural to regret about a failed marriage.

The strange thing is, I haven't thought about it for years, though. Perhaps,' she added wryly, 'I was having my last final fling, a belated wake.'

'Or perhaps,' he said after a moment, 'you were crying because you haven't yet found anyone, Ray Saunders included, who makes you feel the way I did, my sweet Hillary, who used to just love to make love to me.'

She stared at him and felt a nerve begin to beat in her jaw and a cruel flush of heat rising from the base of her throat. '*You* ...' she whispered, then bit her lip and could have died, could have shot herself as she saw the mocking smile that twisted his lips. Oh, we were so serene, we thought, she taunted herself. God ...!

'Bastard?' he supplied quite gently. 'Maybe. I have a reputation for it anyway. But let's go on being honest for a little longer, my dear Hillary. How many men have there been since—us?'

'Doz ...' She stopped abruptly.

He laughed softly. 'Dozens? You tried to tell me that once before. I found no evidence of them then and there's no evidence ...' He too stopped speaking suddenly and something oddly wary flashed in his eyes but was gone immediately.

'Why ... why did you look like that?' she asked, momentarily diverted.

Clive raised his eyebrows and shrugged. 'Like what? You're not trying to change the subject, are you?'

A gust of rage shook her then, and she forgot all about that strange, fleeting look in his eyes. 'How many *women* have there been since us?' she asked deliberately. 'Not counting the ones you had during *us*—as you like to put—of course. We won't bother about them,' she said, with a flippant wave of her hand. 'More than a dozen, two, three? I'm sure you outdid me by a mile!'

'Oh,' he replied amiably, 'I've lost count. None that made much of an impression, I'm afraid. But you're wrong about one thing. Contrary to what I told you, there was no one while we were married.'

'You . . . I . . .'

'Don't believe me? It's true nevertheless, Hillary.'

She stared at him with her lips parted and her eyes stunned. 'Then why did you tell me that? I mean . . . *Why*?'

He looked down at his glass and when he raised his eyes they were sombre and suddenly compassionate, and she knew then that this was the truth, that he had lied.

'Hillary,' he said abruptly, 'there was no way that I could see, that we could have gone on, then. I . . . did you a terrible injustice in the first place. And a blind man could have seen how, between the two of us, your mother and I were tearing you apart. I *knew* I had to end it, and cleanly and quickly. I thought that was the one thing that would really do it.'

She sat back and picked up her wine. 'It did,' she said at last. 'I'm only sorry now it wasn't true,' she added in a cracked, dull sort of voice.

'Why?' He studied her heart-shaped face, so still now, and pale. 'So that you could keep on hating me as much as ever?' he said quietly.

She didn't answer. In truth she didn't know why and, worse, was afraid to think about it, really.

'But we digress,' he murmured what seemed like an age later. 'We were talking about you. Have you slept with Ray Saunders yet?'

'It's none of your business.' She looked up from the ruby depths of her wine at last.

'It is—if you still can't forget . . .'

'Don't say it!' she warned, her eyes suddenly fierce and angry again. 'There is no *us* any more. There never really was! All it was was a very experienced man,' she said bitterly, 'and a little girl who'd been deprived of a normal growing-up. And if it taught me one thing, it was that it's never enough on its own. I learnt that lesson really well. So the last thing I'm looking for with a man is that . . . horribly vulnerable, like putty-in-his-hands kind of feeling I had with *you*.'

'Hillary,' he said roughly, 'you can't marry a man you don't enjoy going to bed with—not even to punish me.' His mouth was grim and his eyes hard.

'I didn't *say* I wouldn't enjoy going to bed with him. I didn't say anything about it at all . . .'

'You wouldn't fool a first-grader, though. But tell me about him, then. Tell me what else he's got to offer?'

'No! Why should I?' Her voice shook with suppressed rage and emotion. 'But I'll tell you something else, and I hope to God you believe me this time. It's none of your business. You have no right to pry into my life any more, to do what you're doing . . .'

'Look,' he said through his teeth, 'today I came upon you quite by accident. *You* were the one who taunted me with my taste in houses and the kind you'd give your eye teeth to own and couldn't resist decorating. You were the one who fell down the steps to get away from me in your supreme embarrassment. Then I held you in my arms and you started to remember what it used to be like, didn't you? Because you've been asleep these past six years, haven't you, Hillary? Like the Sleeping Beauty.'

'You ... No,' she said, her lips white and trembling. 'Just give me my car keys. I'm going home. I don't have to stay and listen to this.'

Clive said nothing, but dug into his pocket and pulled out her key ring and dropped it on the table. Then he said almost idly, 'Why don't you ask yourself why you're so upset, though? And if I were you I'd do it before marrying Ray Saunders.

Hillary could barely speak. But finally she did get out, 'A-And assuming I come up with your answer? What then? Will you give me a crash course in getting over you? Like you gave me a crash course in marriage?'

For a moment his eyes blazed with an anger almost as great as her own. But his words were cool. 'I had some sweet memories of you, Hillary.'

She closed her eyes, in danger of fainting from sheer rage. Then she stood up convulsively, rocking the table violently and knocking over a nest of miniature flags, then she snatched up her car keys and stalked out to the tune of many an amused stare—the place had filled up.

Not that I care, not that I care, she said over and over to herself as she drove home—in fact it became a sort of a catch-phrase which she was still saying as she took a bath and scrubbed herself from head to toe. And later, when she was pacing her bedroom like a caged tiger, wearing only her blue robe. But finally she sank down on to the bed, suddenly exhausted and with the grip of a mad fury, such as she had never before experienced, loosening.

She sat for a time with her hand pressed to her mouth. Then she got up and went across to her oval cheval mirror and stared at herself. Was it an older face? she wondered. Or was it the face of someone who had been asleep for six years?

But all she could see was that it had fined down a bit from what she remembered of her eighteen-year-old face. And that the eyes were different, still a little wild and stormy. Well, she thought, they're different because I wasn't capable then of . . . such emotion. I thought I was, but little did I know. What a way to find out, though!

She bit her lip and half turned away, then on a sudden impulse, turned back and opened her robe and studied her body critically.

It hadn't changed much either. Still as slim and almost fragile as it had been then, and the skin still as soft and silky as when it had bruised and marked so easily beneath Clive's hands and his lips. What had he used to say to her sometimes with a smile lurking in his eyes? 'Did I do that? I'll have to be more careful with that lovely, oh so tender skin, won't I?' And later, sometimes the next morning he would insist on examining her from head to toe. 'There, I'm learning. Not a mark,' he'd say.

She closed her eyes and drew her robe together and turned away properly this time. Then she hugged herself in a kind of agony because, like Pandora's Box, she realised with a wry bitterness, when one memory tumbles out, a lot of others come with it. Such as how her body had responded—for that matter whether he had marked her skin unintentionally or when he was deliberately trying to avoid it.

I need a man—the bleak thought slid into her mind and caused her to flinch with pain and distaste.

But perhaps I do, she found herself thinking then. I'm not a child any more. Perhaps I wouldn't be going through this if I'd at least . . . Oh, hell, she thought hollowly. What *am* I going through?

That's the point. But surely I'm right. It can only be a belated sort of wake. For *myself*. For the fool I was.

'I mean,' she said out aloud, 'how could I possibly really regret Clive Eastman, who thinks he can walk back into my life and take up where he left off? How could I? Because that's what he seems to think.'

'You look . . .' Wendy said the next morning, 'oh, forget it. No good, the Bardon sale?' she added brightly. 'I thought it mightn't be.'

'Actually I found the other half of a . . . of a . . .' Hillary stopped. 'Um . . . a Spode dinner service. Like mine. Only I left it there,' she said on a descending scale, suddenly remembering.

'Well!' Wendy's eyes, which had a tendency to bulge in moments of surprise, did just that. 'It's a funny thing, but there was a carboard carton on the doorstep this morning, with some china in it. And a red hat, like the one you wore yesterday. I . . . It's over there.' She waved a hand.

'Oh. It must have fallen off,' said Hillary, without going over to investigate. 'I mean my hat. Actually, by rights the dinner service should have fallen off, too. But it didn't.'

'If,' Wendy said delicately, 'I knew what you were talking about . . .'

'Nothing!' Hillary interrupted briskly. 'Well, only that we have a relatively rare, full Spode dinner service for sale. I'll get the rest of it.'

'And the hat?'

'The hat . . . I might give that away. It's worthless.' She retreated then, however, her powers to dissemble being curiously depleted, she found.

But she packed up her Spode determinedly despite a slight qualm that her sudden decision to sell it might be a little childish.

It was when she was about to take it back into the shop that she heard her aunt and Wendy talking through the door she had left just ajar.

'Seen Hillary this morning, Mrs Selby?' Wendy was enquiring.

'Why, no. I went in to town very early. But that's why I'm here—I thought she'd be here. Something wrong?'

'Something not right, I'd say,' Wendy replied cryptically.

'Such as?'

'I'm only guessing, of course. But it's one of two things—Clive Eastman or Charles Saunders. My guess is the first.'

Oh God, how transparent am I? thought Hillary, as she stood, momentarily transfixed, beyond the door.

'You know,' Wendy said then with a curiously passionate intensity, 'I can't believe the nerve of the man! To walk back into her life after all this time,' she said indignantly, causing Hillary to wince at this unconscious echoing of her own sentiments, 'after *deserting* her when she was only a baby really . . . I just can't believe it!'

There was a little silence. Then Hillary heard her Aunt Bea say, 'That's not altogether true. Still, you're right.'

She frowned and wondered what her aunt had meant. What wasn't altogether true? Then she realised someone was knocking at her side entrance and she put down the box she was holding, sighed frustratedly, and went to answer the door.

It was Ray.

'Oh!' she gasped, and fell into his arms laughing and crying a little at the same time. 'Oh, I didn't expect you home for another two days!'

He held her tight and laughed. 'I should do this more often—come home unexpectedly!'

She laid her head on his shoulder with her face turned away from him and was stricken with guilt suddenly. And more so when he added, 'Is something wrong?'

'No. Why?'

He set her away from him and looked into her eyes. 'I'm not complaining,' he said softly. 'I've even dreamt of you welcoming me like this one day. But,' he hesitated. 'Forget it,' he said swiftly, then, and bent his head to kiss her.

'So,' she murmured a little later, 'tell me what brought you home early?'

He grinned. 'You.'

'No, seriously, Ray.'

'Seriously, you. And,' he grimaced, 'the fact that I'm going to have to spend another week in Canberra.'

'You could have rung me and told me that.'

'I thought this was a nicer way of doing it. I was right.'

She pressed his hand and turned away. 'Like a cup of coffee?'

'Thanks. Hillary,' he followed her into the kitchen, 'by the way, I'm not going back until tomorrow morning. Will you have dinner with me tonight?'

'I'd love to. Of course I would. Actually, I could take the whole day off.'

'Terrific,' he said, then his face fell. 'I've got to

see my father. Business,' he added gloomily. 'Of both kinds—to do with the firm and politics.'

'Oh well, never mind. Dinner instead of a phone call is more than enough,' said Hillary philosophically. 'But what were you going to ask me? You said, "Hillary," then, "by the way, da-dah da-dah," as if it was an afterthought.'

'I can see,' drawled Ray, reaching for her, 'that my wife is going to be a mind-reader, as well as gorgeous and talented and small and sweet and . . .'

'You're making me blush! Also very curious.'

He considered for a moment, then kissed the tip of her nose. 'I'll tell you tonight.'

'Ray!' she protested, but he stood firm.

'All right, all right. At least tell me where we're going tonight so I know what to wear.'

'Well, there's a new place I've been hearing about that sounds a good spot for . . . engaged couples.' Lovers, he was going to say, she thought, and bit her lip. 'I thought we'd try it. But it's not very dressy. Come as you are.'

'No, I won't!' she laughed, looking down at her jeans and jumper.

'Unless you'd rather we went somewhere really classy. Do you have a yen to get out your glad rags?' he asked seriously.

'Oh, Ray,' she touched his face, '*you're* sweet. No, I think your place sounds perfect.'

Perfect for what I have in mind . . .

Hillary straightened up from her underwear drawer that evening and stood quite still for a time. What do I have in mind? That Ray and I become lovers tonight? Is that why I'm getting out these special things Aunt Bea brought me back from her last trip to Paris? That I've never worn before?

She looked down at the froth of ivory silk and lace in her hands and then crossed to the bed and laid each article out—the almost transparent bra, the lovely little camisole top, the wispy briefs. Honeymoon gear, her aunt had said with a glint in her eye. I wear it all the time . . .

'I don't,' Hillary whispered. 'Oh, mine is pretty enough, but . . .' She fingered the camisole with its tiny row of buttons down the front and narrow satin straps. You wouldn't wear a bra with it, she thought. That would defeat the purpose.

And all of a sudden her mind was filled with images. A man's hands undoing those little buttons one by one as she watched, and sliding the satin straps off. Then she closed her eyes and crumpled the silk in her fingers because it wasn't Ray's hand she saw in her mind's eye but Clive's . . .

'No!' The single syllable was whispered savagely and her face contorted. 'No, no, no! It's going to be Ray, and it's going to be tonight. It's exactly what I had in mind and I should have done it months ago. He *loves* me and I . . . love him. I was stupid to . . . to insist that we wait.'

'You look lovely. Blue suits you.'

Hillary glanced down at the simple woollen dress in a shade that matched her eyes. It had a cowl collar and she had pinned a very old and beautiful silver brooch just below her shoulder. Tiny beaten silver earrings caught the light as she moved her head and her hair swung out, and she wore pale grey stockings and grey suede shoes.

She looked up again and coloured faintly at what she saw in Ray's eyes.

She was a little quiet as the Alfa threaded its way through Paddington. Quiet and absorbed in her curious thoughts. Your place or mine? How *do* you proposition a man, if that's the right word? Even if it's what he wants and what you want? Perhaps it will just come about naturally? Perhaps he'll read it in my face ... Oh God, Hillary, why are you so worried? This is Ray, the man you're going to marry ...

'Here we are,' Ray said lightly. 'It's also handy. If the food's as good as I've heard, we might adopt it.'

Hillary looked out of the window, and froze. It was the restaurant Clive had brought her to last night.

'Ray,' she said jerkily, 'I can't go in there ...' She stopped abruptly as he turned to stare at her. 'I mean ... I'd rather go somewhere else.' They'll remember me for sure, she thought frantically, the waiter, the chef, the receptionist. They'll think I'm mad, coming back with another man after the performance I put on last night. They might not even want to let me in—no, that's crazy, but all the same I'll feel a freak. And there's no way I can sit there without remembering the things Clive said last night, which is the last thing I want to do tonight.

'Hillary, what's wrong? You look as if you've seen a ghost. Have you been here before?'

'I ... Yes.'

'What was wrong with it?'

'Um ... I just didn't like it.'

'The food?'

'The food was ... Well, if you like Italian food, it was fine.'

'I thought you liked Italian food.'

'I do ... sometimes,' she said unhappily. 'But not tonight.'

'I believe they don't only serve Italian food. They have four or five main courses, each a sort of national dish which is superbly cooked. That's why it's called El Cosmo.'

'Oh. Is that what it's called? Well, yes, I get it. Cosmopolitan ...' She closed her eyes, remembering the little nest of flags.

'Hillary.' He frowned down at her. 'I don't understand ...'

She took a breath. 'Ray, just take me somewhere else, please.'

He shrugged after a moment. 'If you say so.'

'That ... was very nice,' Hillary said tentatively, at another restaurant, after a meal she hadn't really tasted.

'I'm glad you approve.'

She flinched. 'I'm sorry.'

'No need to be. Unless you'd like to tell me about it? I thought—I really thought,' said Ray with an effort, 'after the way you greeted me this morning, that we'd finally got to a stage of ... no holds barred. That's why ...' He stopped and sighed and stared down at his plate with his mouth set.

Hillary studied his fair hair which was, as always, neatly trimmed and sleek, and the set of his suit and his hands clasped on the table, and she was conscious of an overwhelming urge to take him in her arms, to comfort him, to be his mother, his sister ...

'That's why what?' she asked instead.

He picked up a fork and started tracing patterns on the tablecloth with it. 'I was going to ask you to forget all this nonsense about finding a house and renovating it first. I was going to ask you to marry me when I get back from Canberra. Who cares where we live? I don't, so long as it's with you.' He looked up.

'A-All right,' she said, and heard her voice as if she was speaking from a long way off.

'Hillary . . .' It was his turn, it seemed, to get up precipitously and rock the table. 'Do you mean that? If you do we'd better get out of here . . .'

'Yes, I do.'

'Come, then.'

'Well, I think we have to pay the bill first. They might not like it if we don't.'

'Oh. Yes. Here.' He thrust a hundred-dollar note into the astonished waiter's hand and hurried her out.

But once in the car he was, it seemed, suddenly a little shy. 'I can't believe it,' he said hesitantly.

'Oh, Ray . . .' The guilt was back. 'That's my fault. I had no right to impose . . . stupid restrictions on us like that.'

'They weren't stupid,' he said, and kissed her throat. 'And I'll stick by them. If that's what you want, for us to be married first, so do I. And— well, Canberra's as cold a place as you could find in Australia at this time of the year. Which is lucky.'

'Ray,' she said softly, and lifted a hand to stroke his hair, 'we don't have to wait.'

He lifted his head and his blue eyes danced suddenly. 'Yes, we do. I've thought about it and longed for it for so long now, I want it to be perfect. And that's what will make it perfect, to know you're my wife . . .'

*   *   *

It was the same cheval mirror Hillary stared into for a second night in a row. After she'd carefully taken off her blue woollen dress and the camisole top she had worn bra-less. And put on her nightgown and her blue robe. It was the same face that stared back at her.

Only it wasn't really. It was a different face. Because the eyes were not a little wild and stormy as they had been last night. Tonight they were confused and, if anything, a little ironic. Your place or mine? she thought, and winced.

But of course that was not all of it. That was only the slightly humorous side to it. Think twice before you set out to seduce a man again, Hillary! As for the . . . suddenly rather frightening prospect of being married, not in the dim and distant future but in the next couple of weeks, hadn't you better think about that, too?

'Hillary, a phone call for you!' Wendy called out the next morning. 'Shall I switch it through to the house or . . .'

'I'm right here,' said Hillary from behind her.

'Oh!' Wendy grinned and lowered her voice. 'It's Mrs Irene Saunders.'

Now I wonder why? Hillary mused with a slight frown as she took the receiver and cleared her throat.

Wendy couldn't hide her curiosity when Hillary put the phone down a couple of minutes later. 'I . . . She wanted me to have lunch with her,' Hillary said. 'But I asked her to come here. I . . . seem to have done a lot of eating out lately. Problem is, what to give her. I've really got a lot of work to get through this morning. Mrs Hocking is champing at the bit about her "den", as she calls it.'

'Why don't you ring up that delicatessen down the road and get them to send up one of their quiches? They're the best I've ever tasted.'

'Oh, great idea! Will do. I don't know what I'd do without you.'

'A lovely lunch, Hillary,' Irene Saunders said warmly, as she dabbed her mouth delicately with a napkin.

'I'm afraid I can't take much credit for it,' Hillary replied wryly. 'All I did was pick up the phone.' She fingered the pink linen tablecloth she had set her gate-legged table with.

'You must give me the name of your delicatessen, then.' Irene's eyes twinkled charmingly.

But beneath the practised charm there was something else, and Hillary had detected it as soon as she had seen her prospective mother-in-law. What was it? she had wondered. A sort of nervous anxiety, she had decided finally, and found herself hoping Irene hadn't come as a second string to Charles Saunders' bow, so to speak. Only to find it was, but not quite in the way she had imagined . . .

'Hillary, I've come to . . . I really wanted to talk to you about Ray. I hope you don't mind,' Irene said abruptly, when they were drinking their coffee. 'I've been getting up the courage . . . I . . .' She tailed off awkwardly, then started again. 'He told me this morning before he left that you were going to get married much sooner that originally planned.'

Hillary stared at the low bowl of fragrant, pale mauve and white sweet peas she had used as a centrepiece for the table. Then she lifted her head. 'Did he?'

'Sh-shouldn't he have? He was so happy . . .'

'No, there's no reason why he shouldn't have. Don't you . . . Doesn't his father approve?'

A dull colour came to Irene's cheeks and Hillary bit her lip. 'I'm sorry,' she murmured.

'That's all right.' Irene stared at her slightly clasped hands for a moment. 'He doesn't know,' she said then. 'Ray didn't tell him and I promised I wouldn't.'

'So . . . he's not going to approve.' Hillary's voice was flat.

'Probably not. He . . . has his reservations about you, I'm afraid. But . . .'

'He . . . I've said this once before,' Hillary interrupted, 'but—well, it's Ray I'm marrying, or more to the point, Ray who wants to marry me. Doesn't his father think he should have some say in the matter?'

'My dear, his father is a . . . very dominating person. It's the way he's made, I'm afraid. And believe me, no one has regretted the day he decided to . . . to accomplish through Ray the goals of—power, I suppose you could say, that he now regrets he didn't seek for himself.'

'Mrs Saunders—Irene,' Hillary whispered, 'that's awful!'

'Yes, it is a bit,' Irene agreed, and stared at Hillary helplessly. 'I've tried to make him see it, but it's like dealing with a . . . with a battering ram. It always has been.'

'Then *why* . . .' Hillary stopped abruptly.

'Why have I put up with it?' Irene smiled sadly. 'Probably because I'm weak and spineless and I've grown used to it, and because I love him. I always have. I'm afraid it can happen to you despite a person's faults.'

There was silence. Until Hillary said in a slightly shaky voice herself, 'I think what we need is something a bit stronger than coffee. Would you like a glass of sherry?' she asked gently.

'I'd love one,' Irene replied, her eyes bright with unshed tears. 'You're very understanding, my dear.'

'Only,' Hillary brought the decanter and two glasses to the table, 'I'm not sure I do understand. How is it going to help Ray if I—back down? Someone—forgive me—but someone has to make a stand . . .'

'Hillary, I've thought about this a lot because Ray means so much to me. In lots of ways he's . . . weathered his father amazingly well. And not in the rather weak way I've done it. But he is . . . I think there's a lot of me in him. And so—and I hope you'll understand that I'm saying this from my heart—I'm not so much concerned about a confrontation with his father over whom he marries. I'm much more concerned that he makes the right choice. For himself.'

'You don't think I am? The right choice?' Hillary queried after a moment.

'I think . . . How can I say it?' Irene's throat worked. 'The thing is, you remind me a little of Charles. You're so very contained sometimes, implacable almost. Strong . . .'

Hillary stared at her incredulously.

'Have I offended you? I'm sorry. It's not that I mean to . . . invest you with Charles' faults. But there's a central core within you, I think, of steel.'

Hillary went on staring at Irene Saunders for a time. Then she blinked and stood up and took her sherry glass over to the window. 'I grew up,' she said huskily, 'in a hard school. If I seem that way,

perhaps that's why.' She swung round suddenly.
'Do I?'

'You . . . That shows through too sometimes.'

'And you think it's not what Ray needs?'

'Well,' Irene hesitated, 'I'm a bit afraid Ray
might have inherited some part of my fatal
fascination for . . . someone like that. But I'm also
afraid it's not the *whole* Ray, as I think he might
one day discover if he meets someone who really
needs him and adores him.'

'I need him,' Hillary said hoarsely.

'Do you? If you're very sure of that, my dear,
I'll say no more. I just want you to think about it
very carefully. And I hope you'll forgive me—
perhaps I should never had done this. But Ray . . .
bears a lot of burdens as it is. You see, I think he
might have told his father to . . . to get lost quite
some time ago if it hadn't been for me.'

'Do you think . . . is he going along with his
political career just because of that?' Hillary asked.

'Well, no. I believe it's like a genuine calling to
him. But I don't believe he has the delusions of
grandeur about it that Charles has.'

Charles has . . . Someone who really needs him
and adores him . . . Implacable almost . . .
Strong . . .

Hillary sat for a long time back at the table after
Irene had left, with her chin in her hand,
pondering.

Had it been genuine motherly concern that had
prompted Irene Saunders, or was it a subtler
orchestration of her husband's views? I don't think
so, she mused. If she was only being a go-between,
she would never had said some of the things she
did.

Then is she right? Am I . . . wrong for Ray? Too . . . *Do* I dominate him? I could have died when she said I reminded her of his father.

She lifted her head at last and stared out of the window. And found herself thinking of Ray with someone like she'd *been* when she was eighteen. Someone he could cherish, someone naïve he could protect—someone he would never have taken no for an answer from, someone who would have loved to have been loved by him.

Then she sighed frustratedly and reflected grimly that, in barely a week, her life had become impossibly entangled. And all because—well, all *since* Clive had come back.

'But at least that's one good thing,' she muttered. 'From the way he dumped my crockery and hat on the front doorstep, I gather I annoyed him enough for him to think twice about . . . interfering any more!'

CHAPTER SIX

'WASN'T quite what I had in mind,' Clarissa Hocking said stiffly, and glared at Hillary over the tops of her bi-focals.

'Then what did you have in mind?' Hillary enquired patiently.

If I had something in mind I wouldn't have called you in, would I?' the old lady replied triumphantly.

Hillary sighed. 'You told me that I had *carte blanche*, but that you'd like to see some final sketches. These,' she waved a hand, 'are the third lot of sketches I've done in as many days which you've rejected. To my mind that indicates that you do have something in mind. If you'd just give me some idea what it is . . . You see, that's the way I prefer to work.' Why, oh, why did I take this impossible old lady on? she asked herself in the same breath—and answered herself in the next, because she's a friend of Aunt Bea's, because she was a bit of a character, something of a very wealthy eccentric—not that I care about the wealthy bit. But she's just an old tartar.

'Dull. Deadly dull,' Mrs Hocking pronounced with a contemptuous glance at the sketches, and Hillary wondered if she'd heard a word of her little speech because she was also deaf.

'Then would you rather have tomato-red walls, a shaggy white carpet, smoked glass and chrome tables and a jade-green brocade settee?' she all but shouted.

'Now! Now you're talking, girl! That's exactly what I'd like. Something lively and a bit shocking. Used to shock a lot of people in my younger days. Tomato-red walls, eh? I like that . . .'

Not only in your younger days, Hillary reflected, and was still grinding her teeth when she got back to the shop.

'What's wrong?' asked Wendy immediately.

'And she also wants a life-size china leopard, two in fact, for either side of the doorway, would you believe?'

'She does? Who does?'

'Dear old Mrs Hocking. Wendy,' Hillary sank into the chair beside the counter, 'I'm losing my touch.'

'And a lot of sleep, by the look of it,' Wendy commented after a moment. 'When's Ray due back?'

'In two more days.' She looked up at Wendy a bit challengingly, but knew immediately that she had underestimated her. For if there was one thing Wendy was superb at, it was knowing when to hold her tongue. It's strange, Hillary thought, the way we met again and became such good friends. Because she is—the best kind of friend one could have. And I should have known she wasn't going to . . . pry. It's just that I feel I could bite the next person who attempts to . . . soliloquise on the subject of Ray and myself, or just me for that matter. Because I've done enough of that in the past week. The only thing is, I haven't come up with . . . I mean I still don't know if his mother mightn't be right.

'Oh, dear,' Bea Selby laughed delightedly. 'Clarrie Hocking must be seventy if she's a day, but she was never one to conform.'

'She wants me to do some more rooms for her,' Hillary said gloomily. She'd washed her hair and then accepted her aunt's invitation to share supper with her, so she was sitting on the floor with her hair still wrapped in a towel and eating macaroni cheese.

Bea's cottage was a rather larger version of Hillary's and the lounge-dining room was divided by a lovely wooden archway. But the fireplace, which every winter Hillary envied immensely, was in the lounge. And on this clear—the rain had finally departed—cold night, two fragrant logs were burning cheerfully in it.

'I should have thought you would enjoy doing some more rooms for her. You could really let yourself go.'

Hillary put her knife and fork together and pushed her plate away, and sighed. 'I don't seem to be enjoying much lately,' she said thoughtfully. She unwound the towel and began to rub her hair.

'Want to tell me about it? Hang on, I'll get the coffee.'

But when her aunt came back, Hillary said suddenly, 'Aunt Bea, I've been meaning to ask you something. I overheard you and Wendy talking the other day in the shop. I wasn't eavesdropping intentionally, but—well, you were discussing me. And Clive.'

'Oh, yes.' Bea put the tray she had brought down on a low table. She wrinkled her brow. 'What were we saying?'

'Wendy was carrying on about what a nerve he had to come back into my life after deserting me and so on.'

'Ah. Yes, I remember now.' Bea poured the coffee and handed Hillary a cup. 'I agreed with her. By the way, is he still . . .'

'No. But it wasn't that you agreed with her that puzzled . . .'

'Actually,' her aunt interjected, 'I don't wholly agree with Wendy on the subject. But she has a fairly conventional soul and I like her, so I didn't want to upset her. If it wasn't that, though, what was it?'

Hillary stared at her with narrowed eyes. 'Say that again. You mean you *do* think he has the right?'

'Let's take one thing at a time,' Bea replied placidly. 'Tell me what puzzled you in the first place. And don't look at me like that, Hillary. I refuse to be provoked.'

'*You* refuse to be provoked!' But Bea only returned her look with one of unruffled blandness. 'All right,' Hillary said then, as if to say, two can play at this game, 'you said something about it not being altogether true—as if he hadn't really deserted me. I mean . . . You know what I mean, divorced me, etc.'

And as she looked at her aunt expectantly, she saw, with some surprise, her face sober curiously. 'Did I say that?' Bea murmured.

'Yes, you did, Aunt Bea.'

Bea Selby got up abruptly and placed another log on the fire. Then she stood staring down at it before coming, or so it looked to Hillary, to a sudden decision.

'My dear, I'm not supposed to tell you this. I promised I wouldn't. Only . . . well, you've half flushed it out of me anyway. What I meant was that Clive wrote to me after he left you. And he tried to explain what had happened. He also . . . I suppose you would call it, appealed to me as someone you were very fond of and vice versa, to try and help you over what had happened.'

Hillary's lips parted. 'He did that?'

'Yes. I still have that letter. And in spite of being
... furious about the whole business, and
incidentally, Hillary, feeling as guilty as hell for
going off that summer and leaving you to the
tender mercies of your mother, who was a neur-
otic ...' she waved a hand, 'in spite of all that, I
was oddly moved by his letter. And, in fact, that was
the start of a ... long correspondence between us.
Oh, we only wrote two or three times a year, but
we were still writing up to a couple of months ago.'

'About ... about me?'

'Yes—well, mostly. Actually it was his sugges-
tion, after your mother died, that I try to interest
you in this kind of business, not mine. Of course,
once he'd made it, I realised it was perfect for
you.'

'But how did he know ... I mean ...'

'He must have known you better than you
thought, my dear.'

'I'm ... I don't know what to say ...'

'Yes. Well, that's probably a pretty common
reaction to finding out someone is not quite as
black as you've painted them.'

Hillary cast her aunt an unfriendly look. But
before she could think of anything else to say,
something dawned on her. 'So that's how he knew
there'd been no one else—you told him?'

'Did he say that?'

'He ... said something about it. I thought he
was just guessing.'

'All I ever told him was that, until you met Ray,
you hadn't formed any serious attachments.'

'And you never,' Hillary asked a shade tartly,
'felt a tremor of guilt about carrying on this
correspondence behind my back?'

'No. Should I have? I thought it was unusually decent of him to be concerned for so long. But then he's an unusual man.'

'He's that all right. It's a pity he didn't ...' Hillary stopped abruptly.

'What?'

'Nothing.' It's a pity he didn't work it all out before we were married, was what she'd been going to say. Then he might not have had to be 'concerned' about me afterwards. She sighed, and thought, not for the first time, anyone would think I was just a talking doll in those days. Perhaps I was?

'Hillary, what are you going to do about Ray?' Bea asked quietly.

'I think—I'm going to marry him,' her niece replied after a time, 'despite everyone's efforts to talk me out of it. Ray is ... I trust Ray and I care about him more than you all realise, perhaps.'

'Who else has tried to talk you out of it? And I haven't precisely ...'

'Yes, you have,' Hillary said kindly. 'And his mother. And, in a roundabout way, his father. Clive ...' She was gazing into the fire as she spoke, but she straightened suddenly and swung round to her aunt.

'You didn't ... you didn't enlist Clive's help, by any chance, Aunt Bea?' she asked softly, but a little menacingly.

'I don't know what you mean.'

'Not in one of those letters you wrote to him?'

'I ...' For once in her life Bea looked a little uncomfortable.

Hillary climbed to her knees. 'You did!' she exclaimed incredulously. 'You told him you didn't approve of Ray ... s-so come home and see what you can do about it kind of thing, seeing you're so concerned about her . . .'

'No, I did not!' Bea interrupted sharply. 'I only told him you were . . . serious about Ray. That's all.'

'Then why did you look so guilty?' Hillary demanded.

'Because I'm beginning to wonder if I should even have done that—in the circumstances,' Bea said a little grimly. 'Only I wasn't to know . . .'

'Oh,' Hillary cried, 'I'm surprised to hear you admit to some qualms. After going behind my back all these years!'

'Hillary,' Bea Selby said angrily, 'don't be a fool. In fact, he came home for quite a different reason, if it makes you feel any better. Although if I were you, I should examine your extreme indignation very closely.'

'What do you mean?' asked Hillary through trembling lips.

'I mean,' Bea replied shortly, 'that you should ask yourself why the thought of Clive at least caring what became of you maddens you so. Is it because you still bitterly, bitterly resent, what he did to you?'

'Why shouldn't I?' Hillary shot back at her aunt, then closed her eyes suddenly, as she saw the trap too late.

But Bea was now in no mood to be merciful. 'Why *should* you? You've got your act together now, quite superbly! You've got a career, and a man who adores you and wants to marry you, a man you trust and care about very greatly—quote, unquote. Why *should* you?'

One of the logs on the fire sent up a shower of green sparks.

'Can I ask you a favour, Aunt Bea?' Hillary said

at last. 'Don't quote me.'

'My dear,' Bea's face softened, 'I'm sorry. I hate to see you in this dilemma.'

'Is it so obvious?'

'To me . . .'

'Why did he come back, then?' asked Hillary after a while. 'He said to retire, but I can't believe that.'

Bea was silent, then she shrugged. 'He might have no choice. He was changing a tyre on his car some months ago when the jack or something slipped and hurt his hand—damaged the tendons or something. His string hand. It's . . . apparently it's good for just about everything else but not the strain of playing the violin as a virtuoso. His fingers stiffen up under that kind of pressure.'

'Oh, God!' Hillary stared at her aunt in horror. 'Why didn't he tell me? There . . . there's no sign . . .'

'If you look very closely there are some scars from operations inside his wrist.'

'Then why didn't *you* tell me?'

'He doesn't want anyone to know and to feel sorry for him. In fact I forced it out of him.'

'You . . . how . . . why?'

Bea sighed and said, 'After the night of your engagement I went to see him and I tried to explain to him about the Saunders and how very difficult he would have made it for you. I also went to find out what his intentions were.'

'He told me,' Hillary said abstractedly, 'that it had come as a great surprise to him—the announcement of our engagement that night. That couldn't have been quite true.'

'Well, it could. Believe me, I did only ever write to him that you had met someone who, for the first time, you seemed . . .'

'Serious about,' Hillary finished drily for her.

'Yes. And although he'd been home for about a fortnight apparently before that charity ball, I hadn't seen him—I was away, if you recall. But there was a note from him . . .'

'Oh. But what will he *do*?' Hillary queried dazedly. 'He'll go mad!'

'I think that's why he came back to Brisbane, to try to work something out.'

'He . . . did that once before,' Hillary said painfully.

'Mmm. I think a homing instinct in times of crisis is a rather human foible. But there's plenty he can do. Compose, teach, conduct . . .'

Hillary shivered suddenly.

Sleep eluded her completely that night. All she could think of was Clive, alone, deserted, his mistress gone for ever . . .

'I came,' she said shakily, '. . . well, I wasn't even sure you'd be here.'

It was late the following afternoon and the last rays of sunlight were reflected in the mullioned windows beneath the gable of the old house in Bardon. His car in the driveway had told her he was there.

'As you see,' Clive said coldly, 'I am.'

Hillary licked her lips and contemplated taking flight. Then, because he was wearing a pair of jeans and a grey sweater and his hair looked untidier than normal, she found herself asking if he'd moved in.

'Yep. Like to have a look? Of course it's not up to your standard.' He eyed her mockingly.

'Yes, I would.'

But she soon understood the reason for that mocking look. For there was hardly anything to see apart from the fact that the walls had been stripped and painted ivory, with white woodwork, and the old floral carpet replaced by smooth, velvety, wall-to-wall stuff of the finest quality in a pale aquamarine throughout. But of furniture there was the bare minimum. A leather sofa in the lounge in a soft champagne colour, a bed and a wardrobe in one bedroom and a pine table with four chairs in the kitchen was all there was. Even the telephone in the hall sat on the floor.

'What . . . what will you do with the servants' quarters?' she asked as the silent, supremely awkward—for her—tour appeared to end in the kitchen.

'I've had them converted to a studio,' he said briefly.

'Can I see it?'

He shrugged after a moment. 'If you want to. What is this, Hillary? Have you changed your mind?'

She fingered the buttons of her jacket. In deference to old Mrs Hocking, whom she had just been to see and who might have startling ideas on a host of subjects but always dressed very formally, she had donned an oatmeal tweed tailored suit over a taupe silk blouse, and wore well-polished brown leather shoes.

'I think you've started well enough without me,' she said, and added lamely, 'I would have done the walls the same.'

His grey eyes glinted sardonically as he studied her, the neat suit and the fine gold chain around her neck revealed by the open collar of her shirt, the pale stockings and plain but elegant shoes and back to the gold slide in her hair. 'How kind of you,' he murmured then, and led the way out of the kitchen on to the walkway.

Oh, God, I should never have come, Hillary thought dismally. He's in an impossible mood!

And his studio was in a state of impossible chaos, she saw, as she stood just inside what was now one big, light and airy room. Or would be when relieved of its clutter. Because at a glance it seemed to contain all his possessions—paintings stacked against the walls, books everywhere, music overflowing from the top of a baby grand piano and covering every inch of a big solid table that had a dent in one corner as if someone had taken a swipe at it. A chess set she remembered; suitcases with clothes spilling out of them; an open brown paper parcel on the floor near her feet containing brand new sheets and towels.

She looked around and then up at him with a slight smile. 'You're in a mess!'

'The rest of the furniture's arriving tomorrow,' he said shortly. 'I'll have somewhere to put everything then. But if you were thinking of offering to do it for me, don't bother. The job's been taken.'

'I wasn't,' she replied quietly. 'The . . . lady in the red dress?' she asked.

Clive raised his eyebrows. 'What red dress?'

'Your companion at the ball,' she said straightly. 'I thought she might . . .' She shrugged. 'Be with you. Someone ought to be . . .'

'Oh, her,' he said. 'No, I've employed a "daily". She also arrives tomorrow. The lady in the red dress was only a good friend as matter of fact, from way back.'

'I don't remember her,' said Hillary, then bit her lip.

'You didn't know her. She was overseas in our time. Now she's an airline executive, is separated from her second husband and only into men as an occasional diversion—so she says.' He smiled unpleasantly. 'It was she who had the tickets for that ball and she who persuaded me to go. Satisfied?'

Hillary turned away. Then she bent down as she noticed that a violin was protruding from beneath the parcel of linen.

'Leave that, Hillary,' he said sharply.

It was too late. She'd pulled it free carefully and straightened up with it in her hands. But it was a broken violin, with splinters of wood sticking up from where it looked for all the world as if it had been savagely dashed against something solid. She stared at it and then glanced at the dented corner of the table—and knew with a sick certainty that Clive, who had often taken his frustrations out on inanimate objects but never on his violins, had done just that. Dashed it against the table in a fury of despair.

'I'm so very sorry,' she whispered.

He had followed her swift glance from the shattered violin in her hands to the table and back. 'Sorry for what?' he asked softly but menacingly, with his eyes narrowed and glittering.

'For what happened to your hand.'

His mouth set in a pale, hard line. Then he said, 'Never trust a woman. She shouldn't have told you.'

'She ... I don't see why not. I mean, I can understand why you don't want the whole world

to know . . . I don't think I would, either. But . . .'
She hesitated.

He stared down at her. 'But what? Why should I
want your sympathy more than anyone else's?'
And the old autocratic, heavy-lidded look was
there again, the same one, contemptuous and
impatient and sardonic, that had shrivelled her up
years ago.

Only I've grown up, she thought, surely? She
put the violin down on a suitcase and said evenly,
'Clive, don't hate me for feeling sorry for you.
After all, you're not above that emotion, are you?'

'What the hell do you mean?'

'Well, you felt sorry for me for a long time,
didn't you? The letters you wrote, the career you
suggested—you must have felt a sense of sorrow,
regret, something. Why shouldn't I feel the same?'
Only, an inner voice mused, you found it hard to
accept, too, Hillary.

'I still feel sorry for you, Hillary.'

It wasn't what she expected to feel in the
circumstances. Yet his words seemed to evoke a
floodtide within her and not only his words—the
pitying look that had accompanied them, combined
with that sort of contemptuous hauteur he did so
much better than anyone else she had ever known.
And it taught her one thing, she found—that she
must have grown up, because she no longer felt
shrivelled at all, she felt wildly, hotly angry . . .

But all this occurred to her in a flash—about as
long as it took to lift her hand and connect it with
the side of his face in a manner similar to the way
the violin on the suitcase beside her must have met
the corner of the table.

For a long moment, though, as her arm sank
back to her side, her hand stinging, she found

herself wondering if she might not live to see another day. Because it seemed she might have evoked a fury herself, only greater than her own, and infinitely more powerful . . .

But what Clive did next took her completely by surprise. He jerked her into his arms and started to kiss her. Only she soon realised it was quite different from any way he'd ever kissed her before because it was hard, and bruising—a savage kind of revenge in fact that left her limp in his arms when he finally lifted his head, her face white, her eyes glazed with fear.

'Oh God,' he said huskily, gazing down at her, 'what have I done? Don't look like that! I'm sorry . . .' And he cradled her to him. 'I'm sorry,' he said again into her hair. 'The thing is . . . I think I'm going mad. I can't . . . I just can't believe it's happened to me. Yet it was meant, I know. I got a flat tyre in the middle of nowhere with an almighty blizzard threatening—the only options I had were to try and change it, although the road was already like glass, or wait and probably freeze to death. Perhaps it's what I should have done, though . . .'

'No . . . Clive, no,' she whispered, and raised shaking fingers to his face to find it wet with tears. 'It can't ever be that bad. You mustn't let it.'

But in her heart, as he held her to him tightly and she felt the shudders that racked his body, she knew there was nothing she could say that would help, no words that could touch this agony. And she thought dimly that he had probably not, until now, admitted even to himself the depth of it. So let it all pour out, my darling, she said to him in her mind. At least it will be some kind of a release.

But in the next instant, she knew instinctively

how she could really help him to release that
savage, violent agony and hurt, at least for a
time . . .

It was dark when she awoke.

Then after a while her eyes adjusted to a thin
edging of moonlight around the room, coming in
from the uncurtained bedroom window.

Clive was asleep beside her, his head on her
shoulder, one arm around her, his breathing deep
and even. She lay for a long time staring upwards
and contemplating what she had done, deliberately . . .

It was as if he had known what was in her mind
almost as soon as she had. She had felt it in the
way his hands had moved on her body. Then he
had tensed and half-pushed her away and she had
realised that he hadn't read her mind at all, only
his, and she had slid her arms around his waist
and laid her cheek on his heart.

'Hillary . . .' He had said her name on a breath.

'Don't talk,' she had whispered. 'Hold me . . .'

'I can't . . . I . . .'

'Yes, you can. I want you to, like this.' She had
felt for his hand and lifted it to place it on her
breast beneath her jacket. Then she had raised her
face like a flower to the sun. 'Kiss me.'

Clive had moved convulsively and for a while
she had found it difficult to breathe, he had held
her so hard.

What had followed had been blurred and dazed
for her. He had made love to her with passionate
intensity and for him, she'd thought, when she was
able to think clearly at all, it had been exactly
what she'd intended—a physical release for his
mental anguish. For her, it had been something

else. She had held him and cradled him and comforted him as if he was bereaved, never faltering, and letting him have his will with her body in a strong surge—a final, she'd hoped, tilt at bitter fate.

But he hadn't gone to sleep then, not then, although she had thought he had. Sleep had eluded her, though, as she had lain very still, feeling fragile and a little like a shell-shocked survivor of some conflict. Not only his, but her own.

Not the best way to take up sex after a six-year lay-off, she had reflected, and finally moved gingerly.

And that was when she'd realised Clive hadn't fallen asleep, because she'd heard him say almost beneath his breath, 'Oh God, I've done it again! Hillary—you shouldn't have let me . . .'

'Yes, I should,' she had whispered shakily, but had turned her face into his shoulder to hide it. Only she had raised it almost immediately and smiled at him. 'It's not as if we've never done it before. So don't say another word! If you can't do it for an ex-husband in times of need, who can you do it for?'

He had captured her face in his hands and smudged an errant teardrop that was sparkling on her lashes, 'If ex-husbands also have some rights in times of need, will you at least allow this one to return the compliment, then? Come,' he'd said, and taken her into his arms and pulled the blankets up. 'Comfortable?'

'Clive . . .' her breath had caught in her throat, 'you don't have to . . .'

'Yes, I do. Go to sleep,' was all he had said, but he had stroked her hair and held her like a child.

And it was as if she had been transported back through the years to a younger version of herself who had not known the sweetness of love until a tall man with imperious grey eyes and an arrogant mouth had shown her. And shown her, as well, deeper into a side of his nature few knew. The side that possibly warred often with the more obvious elements of it, those elements you couldn't help seeing in every inch of his dynamic, tempestuous bearing. The side that could be so gentle, that could make you tremble with love . . .

Did I fall asleep thinking that? Hillary asked herself as she stared at the ceiling in the thin moonlight. Or doing it?

And she trembled then as a cold sense of fear clutched her heart. I must have been mad! I've got to get out of here.

'Hillary?' His sleep-drugged voice stilled her sudden urgent movement and made her heart start to pound.

Oh God, the last thing I want to do is wake him, she thought, and lay as still as a statue, trying not to breathe, even. But the damage had been done.

'Sweet Hillary,' he murmured, and started to kiss her bare shoulder. 'So sweet—you haven't really changed.'

'Clive . . . Clive, don't,' she whispered despairingly as his mouth slid over her smooth skin.

'Don't what?' He lifted his head and stared down at her heart-shaped face on the pillow.

'D-don't do this,' she said huskily, with her lips quivering.

He raised a hand and pushed a strand of hair off her face, then cupped her cheek. 'Isn't it part of the arrangement?'

'No . . .'

'I think it ought to be. It's what I had in mind anyway. You hadn't done this for a long time, had you, Hillary?' he said gently.

'I . . . No . . .'

'Since . . . you and I?' He traced the outline of her mouth and slid his hand down the side of her throat.

She closed her eyes.

'Hillary?'

'No,' she whispered, 'not since then. But . . .'

'Then we can't just leave it like that. I must have hurt you . . .'

'Not really—no, you didn't.'

'I can imagine,' he said with a tinge of irony. 'I used to only have to touch you to leave a bruise.' His wandering fingers were back at her throat, then sliding down to her breasts. 'But anyway, it couldn't have been any good for you. These used to remind me of little buds . . . I think they've matured now, they feel fuller, but still high, and still chaste. Perhaps I can do something about that. I used to be able to.'

'Clive,' she breathed, as her nipples started to tingle beneath his fingers, 'no, you mustn't. Please don't . . . Oh God, you don't understand!'

'Don't talk,' he muttered against the corner of her mouth. 'Didn't you say that to me earlier?'

'Yes . . . but . . .'

'Hold me, instead. We can talk about it later . . .' And he kissed her lips and then her breasts and, in the way it had once been for her, the blood started to beat through her body and neither six long years nor the fact that she was engaged to another man altered in the slightest the way her body responded to the man who had once played it like a virtuoso.

Later, she kept saying in her mind, later might be too late, too late . . .

They slept again afterwards, in each other's arms. And the sun was shining when they woke. Hillary moved her head on his shoulder and trailed her fingers down his arm.

'How do you feel?' he asked softly.

How do I feel? she wondered. Warm and soft . . . relaxed . . . as if I never want to get up . . .

He tilted her chin upwards gently and she stared at him, her eyes grave but curiously peaceful. 'I think I might have needed that,' she said huskily. 'You were right. But . . .' She hesitated.

'It doesn't change anything,' he said after a while. 'Is that what you're trying to say?'

'Oh, Clive, how can it?' she whispered. 'It was always like this—so good in bed, but out of it . . . I'm still not the right person for you.'

He started to speak, then seemed to change his mind. 'Still,' he said finally, 'I'm glad we've made up, in a manner of speaking.'

Hillary was silent for a long time. Then she said with a shimmer of tears in her eyes, 'So am I. Have you . . . made any plans?'

He sighed and kissed her hair. 'Ned's made all sorts of plans for me. I think I'll probably turn to conducting and composing—I always did fancy myself with a baton. But for between times, or in case it doesn't work out, I'm looking for a property where I can breed horses.'

'You mean—you'll sell this house?'

'No. I'll keep it as my Brisbane base.'

They were quiet for a time. Then Hillary stirred. 'Aunt Bea will be wondering what's become of me. Wendy too.'

'What will you tell them?'

'Oh, I think I'll preserve a mysterious silence on the subject.'

'Might be wise,' he said with a grin.

But when Hillary was dressed and ready to leave, things turned unexpectedly awkward between them.

'If,' he said, 'there are any ... consequences for you as a result of last night, you would tell me, wouldn't you, Hillary?'

'Con ...' She caught her breath. 'You mean ...'

'Yes. If you find yourself pregnant.'

'I ...' She licked her lips. 'Yes, of course.'

'Then I guess this is goodbye, Hillary.' He was standing across the room from her wearing the same jeans and pullover he had had on yesterday. He had made her a cup of coffee while she had showered, but for some reason she found it hard to swallow, so it sat, barely tasted, on the table.

'Yes ...' she whispered.

He came round the table. 'If you—have cause to change your mind ever ...'

'No, Clive. Let me go, please.'

'All right. I'm sorry,' he said, his grey eyes dark and shadowed. 'But you're probably right, I'd only make your life hell again, more so than ever now. Goodbye, and thank you ...' And he bent his head and kissed her lips gently. Then he turned away and she fled.

But instead of driving home she found herself rather aimlessly heading towards the city and then the Valley, because it was curiously soothing to have to be concentrating on the traffic. Then she noticed a sign that indicated the Bruce Highway that led north to the Sunshine Coast and she took the turn-off thinking, why not? A bit of country air might do me good.

But a bit farther on she had to stop for petrol and, on a sudden impulse, checked her purse to find she only had fifty dollars. But I've got my bankcard, she thought.

She glanced around for a phone box and moments later was ringing her Aunt Bea.

'Hillary! I was worried about you.'

'I'm sorry, Aunt Bea. I'm fine, but can I ask you a favour? Can you hold the fort for me for a couple of days? I . . . I really need a break.'

'I . . . Hillary, are you on your own?'

'Yes, and I *need* to be,' she said into the phone.

'All right.' Her aunt's voice was suddenly brisk. 'Trust me, dear. Take care of yourself.'

'I will,' Hillary said tremulously. 'You're an aunt in a million!' She put the phone down. Then she suddenly remembered that Ray was due home today. How could I have forgotten? she wondered. But there's no way I could face him today, anyway, so perhaps this is for the best after all. Oh, Hillary!

She drove north with her thoughts in turmoil, but as the countryside became less inhabited it was as if her weary mind switched off gradually and by the time the road had begun to wind through State Forests of the Landsborough Shire, dark green and secretive on both sides, she began to relax. Then she caught her first glimpse of the Glass House Mountains, those strange and stunning rocky fingers that towered hundreds of feet into the air and rejoiced in sometimes stranger names, like the tongue-twister Mount Tibrogargan, and she found herself actually smiling and thinking, it's what I do need, a break and a change of scene.

She considered taking the Caloundra turn-off, and then the Mooloolaba one, but in the end she drove all the way to Noosa, beautiful Noosa Heads. And she booked into a motel on the beach, showered because she felt stiff from the long drive, and tumbled into bed naked as a deep exhaustion overcame her, although it was only mid-afternoon.

And she slept deeply and dreamlessly.

CHAPTER SEVEN

'CLIVE ...'

She murmured the name drowsily and moved luxuriously in the soft bed, seeking a long smooth back to stroke and kiss. Then she sat bolt upright with her heart pounding and a fearful sense of revelation seizing her as she saw, with a perfect clarity, what she had done to herself.

'No,' she whispered, lying back slowly and clutching the sheet tightly. 'Oh no ... don't do this to me! I thought ... all through yesterday, when I woke up in his arms, when I left him, it was as if what happened was like ... being exorcised. Now, it's just as if I'm starting all over again, alone again, with only the memories and another wall to build. Oh God! Why did I do it?'

She turned her head into the pillow and started to weep with despair.

Several hours later she was walking along the beach, in a pair of shorts and a jumper she had just purchased, together with some other necessities, oblivious of the crashing of the surf and the few hardy souls—probably from Victoria where it was freezing at this time of the year—who were actually bathing. And as she walked she was arguing with herself tormentedly, anguishedly ... I don't even know—did he mean for us to get married again? He's never really said it, but perhaps it goes without saying. I *do* know, though, I couldn't do it; I'd be mad even to think of it!

But at least you're older now, Hillary, more able to stand up to him . . .

Perhaps, she retorted acidly to this inner voice. But who wants to spend the rest of their life standing up to someone? And don't try to tell me *he's* changed, because I always knew he had a bit of Dr Jekyll and Mr Hyde in him. Well, almost always knew. That's what makes him so . . . so wonderful sometimes and impossible at others. Is that what you want for yourself again? That terrible see-saw? Only a fool would!

She said this to herself with a furious bitterness and the fool within her withered and blanched. To long for someone physically, she added, following up this advantage ruthlessly, is by by no means the whole story. It's also fairly transitory. I mean, you got over that before, you didn't pine away or go into a decline or get odd and start talking to plants or acquiring cats by the dozen. You didn't do any of those things. You only . . .

She stopped walking and stared blindly out to sea, biting her lip. You only, she thought bleakly, never could imagine yourself with another man until Ray came along, and even then by no stretch of the imagination did you fall into his arms . . .

The beach had ended, she discovered, so she climbed a little way up a rocky outcrop and sat down and tried to think about Ray. Only to discover it didn't seem possible. And to make matters worse, she found herself saying conversationally, as the tears streamed down her face, 'Well, Mum, you were wrong about one thing. It seems I'm not like my charming but faithless father after all! Who knows, I might end up staying faithful to Clive for the rest of my life!'

* * *

The three days she spent at Noosa, however, saw her qualifying this strangely terrifying prospect; gradually, and finally, on her last afternoon there, coming to a decision.

There was movement everywhere, it seemed, on that sunny winter's afternoon as she sat on her favourite perch and watched the waves crashing at the foot of the outcrop, sending a silvery net of foam and spray into the air.

A flock of seagulls was busy on the beach around a lone fisherman who was cleaning his catch. They were bobbing about, then rushing forward as he threw away a head, to retreat in squabbling disorder with the titbit. And a busy breeze was ruffling the foliage about her and the surface of the ocean so that it danced and glittered beneath the clear blue of the sky. Out to sea, birds she didn't know the name of were circling high and lazily and then plummeting with a heart-stopping suddenness down through the bright air like arrows, into the water. It was a while before she realised they were fishing and not committing suicide.

'I'll have to tell Ray,' she said out aloud. 'I'll have to tell him what happened and I'll have to try to explain to him *how* it happened and why it changes nothing.' Well, it does. Because I know now I can't really hate Clive any more ... But above all, if Ray still wants to go on ... Oh hell! How *do* you explain to a man that you love him even while another man holds a terrible fascination for you? Do you ask him for more time? Could he ever understand? She sighed suddenly. 'I can only try ...'

'Well, Hillary,' said Bea Selby, surveying her

niece critically, 'feeling better?'

Twenty minutes earlier Hillary had run her car into the garage and she was now in her bedroom unpacking a colourful canvas holdall that was almost new.

'Yes, Aunt Bea.'

'I gather,' her aunt surveyed the pile of clothes on the bed and the new hairbrush and toilet gear, 'that you didn't go prepared for this little jaunt?'

'I . . . No.' Hillary straightened up and grinned. 'Thanks for holding the fort, by the way. I really appreciate it.'

She stretched and to the observant eye, which indeed Bea's was, she looked weary but relaxed. Or is it . . . numbed? Bea wondered with a faint frown.

'Any crises?' asked Hillary.

Bea grimaced. 'Only the whole world and its wife determined to have speech of you,' she said ironically. Then she smiled. 'I preserved a stoical disposition and said you'd had to go off at a moment's notice on serious business and hadn't even had time to tell me where—not quite true, that bit, but I was relieved not to know. It helped with Ray. Want to tell me about it?' She looked at Hillary enquiringly.

'I . . . Not just yet,' Hillary said quietly. 'Do you mind?'

'Not at all. No . . .' Bea waved a hand, 'I'm not hurt! Take your time—and I mean that. Instead,' she rolled her eyes, 'I'll tell you who's been calling—apart from Ray, several times a day.' She reeled off some names, then took an impressive breath. 'Now for the big guns. Clarrie Hocking— for two reasons. She wants her lounge—den—

done in time for her seventy-second birthday which is in—wait for it, one week's time.'

'Oh God!' Hillary groaned.

'Mmm. The second reason is a bit better. She wants us both to go to it. Now one thing to be said for Clarrie Hocking, she gives great parties. She knows more interesting people than you and I put together.'

'But one week!'

'Is it impossible?'

'Well . . . I guess not,' Hillary said wryly. 'And I suppose she's going to hound me to death anyway, so I might as well. It all depends if I can come up with two leopards she likes the look of, actually. She wasn't enthralled by the expressions of the last two I got—said they looked meek and anyway they weren't leopards. They were cheetahs. Did you know that cheetahs have spots but leopards rosettes? I didn't. Who else rang?'

'Martin Wessels.'

'Who's he? You don't mean *the* Martin Wessels?' Hillary's eyes widened.

'None other,' Bea agreed. 'Great Australian film director in person.'

Hillary sank on to the bed. 'What did he want? Or didn't he say?'

'I . . . er . . . persuaded him to confide in me,' Bea replied with a twinkle. 'They say curiosity killed the cat. He wants you to do some interiors for the new film he's making right here in good old Brissy.'

'But I'm not a set designer,' Hillary protested a little faintly.

'Not sets precisely. They've bought an old house which is going to be *the* set—one of them, anyway—and they want it furnished authentic

eighteen-seventies. I told him they couldn't make a
better choice than you!'

Hillary was silent, digesting this.

'How does it sound?' asked Bea.

'It sounds . . . fascinating.'

'Thought it might. Why don't you give him a
ring now? I believe he has to go to Sydney
tomorrow.'

'I . . . I will. I also have to ring Ray.' Hillary
stared down at her hands and twisted her
engagement ring. She glanced up and caught her
aunt narrowing her eyes speculatively.

There was silence for a moment. Then Bea said,
'I'm afraid you can't do that, my dear. He's in Fiji,
you see. He left this morning. That's why—well,
why he was in a worse state, perhaps.'

'Fiji?' Hillary said blankly.

'Yes. Unexpected business which he couldn't get
out of. Apparently it's some sort of extension of
what he was doing down in Canberra. And there's
the possibility that he might have to fly on to
America. I—as I said, it's probably just as well I
didn't know where you were or I might have
succumbed. But he did say he'd ring tonight at
eight o'clock our time.'

'Oh.'

'You'll be here?'

'Yes . . . of course.' Hillary closed her eyes and
wondered if this was how you felt when you got a
reprieve from a life sentence. Then she thought
intensely, but it's only going to prolong the agony.
And he must be so confused. Oh God . . .

'Hillary?'

She opened her eyes. 'I feel a little guilty,' she
said tremulously.

Bea opened her mouth to speak but shut it. Let

her tell me in her own good time, she mused. But it doesn't look good for Ray Saunders. Now I wonder why?

'Ray, I'm really sorry,' Hillary said into the phone that night. 'I just—it was a spur-of-the-moment decision. I felt as if I simply had to get away on my own for a little while.'

'What happened? Something must have happened to make you feel that way, Hillary,' Ray said intensely.

Hillary winced. 'Ray . . .' she began.

'You're having second thoughts about us getting married, aren't you?'

'I . . . yes,' she said very quietly.

'Hillary,' his voice was suddenly decisive and crisp, 'I know why. It's what my mother said to you, isn't it?'

'Your . . . how . . . how did you know that?'

'Never mind,' he said briefly. 'Just do me one favour—let me speak for myself. I thought, actually, you had the sense not to be put off by my parents,' he added with a curious bitterness.

Hillary bit her lip. 'I have,' she said huskily. 'But . . .'

'Good,' he interrupted. 'Then will you do me that favour?'

'Do you . . .?'

'Yes, let me speak for myself, but not over some damned long-distance telephone line. Look, Hillary, I don't know when I'll be back, but I'm straining every nerve to make this trip as brief as possible. At least, if you feel anything for me at all, give me a chance to be with you before you . . . make any decisions. Is that too much to ask?'

'Oh, Ray!' She brushed away some unbidden tears. 'No, it isn't, but . . .'

'Will you do that?' he said insistently.

'A-All right.'

There was a small silence. Then he said in a difficult voice, 'I love you, Hillary,' and the phone went dead.

She put the receiver down and wiped her nose on the back of her hand and thought, oh God, oh God! What am I going to do? I should hate him to think it's because of his parents because, of all people, I know . . . about that. On the other hand, if I tell him about Clive, that's going to hurt him, too. More, or less?

She turned away from the phone, hugging herself anguishedly. And on top of all this, I've taken on Martin Wessels' job, which is the last thing I should have done if I can't concentrate.

One week later, Hillary found herself staring into a boutique window with not much interest, as it was Clarissa Hocking's birthday party that evening and she'd decided that something new to wear might lift her spirits, but couldn't for the life of her decide what.

'The blue,' a voice said behind her. 'It would be sensational with your eyes.'

Hillary turned with her eyes wide and found the large bulk of her new boss, in a manner of speaking, standing behind her.

'Mr Wessels!' she exclaimed in surprise.

'Call me Martin, Hillary,' he answered with a grin. 'Is it for a special occasion?' he added.

'I'm going to a birthday party tonight,' she told him a little wryly.

His penetrating blue eyes narrowed faintly. 'Funny you should say that—so am I. Oh God, don't tell me . . .'

'Not Mrs Hocking's?'

They spoke together than burst out laughing. 'Really,' Martin Wessels said finally, 'she gives great parties. One just . . . finds her a little overpowering, I guess. Is that why you were looking—a little glum?' he asked delicately.

'One of the reasons,' Hillary confessed. 'I've seen a great deal of her this week.' She explained why. 'And to top it off,' she went on, 'the room is really wild, but she loves it and I've got the horrible feeling she's going to tell everyone who did it. I might,' she added ruefully, 'suddenly find myself without any prospective clients.'

'I doubt that. You were very highly re-commended to me, Hillary. I also took the liberty of having dinner at the restaurant you created. I thought it was superb.'

'Why, thank you,' Hillary said gratefully and, for the first time since she'd taken on the film job, found herself thinking of it really objectively, and deciding she was going to enjoy working for this large, untidy man who many said was a genius.

'But to get back,' Martin Wessels murmured, 'see that blue velvet suit not actually in the display but . . .' He pointed and she nodded after a moment. 'Well, I think it might have been made for you,' he finished.

'Do you really think so?'

'Go and try it on,' he advised, 'and see if I'm not right. And in the meantime, I'll see you tonight!' And he walked away with a wave and a grin that was almost a grimace.

Hillary couldn't help laughing again and, with curiously heightened spirits, entered the shop.

And for the rest of the day she found herself feeling slightly more ebullient than she had for some time. It dawned on her, after she had had a bath and started to get ready for the party, why. At least one area of her life was not in a state of turmoil—her work. And it's consoled me before, she thought, so why not let it help now?

She dried herself off properly and hesitated, glancing towards the blue velvet suit hanging outside her wardrobe. That it had been made for her, she knew wasn't possible. All the same, she'd been unable to suppress a pulse of excitement when she'd tried it on in the shop because it seemed to suit her beautifully, besides being a thing of beauty in its own right.

'And as such,' she murmured with a faint grin. 'it deserves the best ...' She opened a drawer of her dresser and pulled out the French silk underwear. 'Who knows, I might even be more successful about wearing it this time,' she added a little mockingly. 'Perhaps some stunning stranger will fall desperately in love with me on sight and have to have his way with me ... Oh God, Hillary, I think you're going round the bend,' she told herself, but found herself laughing at her foolish fancies just a little.

Once in the suit, though, she couldn't help blessing Martin Wessels, not only for complimenting her work and cheering her up slightly but also for having the eye of a connoisseur in regard to clothes. The rich pile of the velvet was one shade darker than her eyes and the fitted jacket flared out slightly over her hips and the pencil-slim

skirt, and it had long slim sleeves, padded
shoulders, and a high neckline with a tiny stand-up
frill in a watermark taffeta of the same colour.

She had changed her hairstyle slightly, brushed
it back more so that her ears were revealed,
because no sooner had she bought the suit than
she had thought of her mother's pearl drop
earrings and exquisite, matching pearl ring and
brooch.

'I was right,' she murmured as she surveyed
herself in the mirror. 'There's something about
velvet and pearls . . .'

There was also, she was forced to acknowledge,
something quite stunning about the way the blue
velvet matched her eyes and the way it highlighted
her creamy skin.

All of which her aunt confirmed some minutes
later. 'Wow!' she exclaimed. 'My dear, I'm almost
speechless. You look . . . just incredibly elegant
and beautiful!'

Hillary sketched a curtsy. 'The same goes for
you, too,' she said, and meant it, for her aunt was
looking magnificent in a black silk dress that not
only looked as if it did, but did in fact come from
Paris, and her grey hair was piled regally on top of
her head.

Bea Selby chuckled. 'We'll show Clarrie Hocking
a thing or two, won't we?'

But it turned out that Clarissa Hocking was the
one with all the surprises up her sleeve.

The first of them came in the form of Ray's
parents, and in fact Hillary had been enjoying the
party until they arrived, a bit late. Enjoying it
because of Martin Wessels, who had come up to
her and said, 'More, more than even I imagined!'

'The room?' she had asked warily.

He had laughed. 'No, the suit. You look very lovely, my dear. As for the room, I think it's magnificently ... exotic. Not to mention,' he had lowered his voice, 'just perfect for Clarrie.' And he had proceeded to take Hillary under his wing.

Then the Saunders arrived and Hillary, catching sight of them across the room, knew that something was wrong immediately, despite her surprise, not to mention dismay, at seeing them. For one thing, Irene Saunders looked as if she'd aged ten years in the space of a few weeks.

'Know them?' asked Martin Wessels, following her startled gaze.

'My ... my parents-in-law. To be, that is,' she stammered. '*No!*' she gasped in disbelief as two more latecomers strolled into the room.

'Hell!' muttered Martin Wessels. 'Am I seeing things or is that Clive? Clive Eastman?'

'No. I mean, you're not seeing things,' Hillary said with an effort, for a moment feeling faint.

'Then you know him, too? He and I go way back!'

'So do ... he and I,' Hillary said hollowly, and watched, unable to tear her eyes away, as Clarissa Hocking descended on Clive delightedly—Clive in a dark suit with a suede waistcoat and a pin-striped shirt, Clive looking amused and quizzical as he responded to the old lady's greetings and introduced her to his companion, Clive looking intensely alive ...

Hillary shivered suddenly and looked away.

'Are you all right?' Martin Wessels asked with a sudden frown. 'You look as if you've seen a ghost. Did you,' a look of curiosity crossed his face, 'say you knew him, too?'

'Yes. I'm fine!' She forced herself to smile brightly as she answered his first question last. 'Who . . . I wonder who that is with him?'

Martin Wessels turned briefly and his expression lightened. 'Blow me down! I didn't recognise him at first, but it's old Ned Cartwright! Don't think I've ever seen him out of London. It's amazing,' he marvelled, 'such a dry-looking little man, but he has on his books some of the world's hottest properties. I'm going over to say hello. Coming?'

'Er . . . no. That is, I will in a minute. I see my aunt over there . . . beckoning me.' This was not altogether true but the best she could come up with and, as her companion had his back to Bea Selby, it came off.

'All right,' Martin Wessels said genially. 'Now didn't I tell you that old Clarrie gives great parties? If anyone can liven up a party, Clive can. Catch up with you just now, Hillary.'

'Yes,' Hillary murmured, and walked a little blindly over to where her aunt stood in deep conversation with an elderly gentleman. 'If anyone can, he can . . .'

'My dear,' queried Bea Selby, looking up, 'is something wrong?'

'Yes. Clive's here. *And* the Saunders. I'm going to slip away if I can. Would you mind making excuses for me if anyone notices?'

Bea blinked. 'Er . . . not at all. Only I'm afraid it's too late . . . Charles,' she said, looking over Hillary's shoulder, 'how are you?'

'Very well, thank you, Mrs Selby,' Charles Saunders answered in what struck Hillary as curiously clipped tones as she turned slowly, reluctantly.

And she took a startled breath as she gazed up

into the eyes of her father-in-law to be. For they were colder than anything she'd ever seen. And all for her, she knew instinctively.

'Well, Hillary,' he said. 'I didn't expect to see you here.'

'There's no reason why Hillary shouldn't be here,' Irene Saunders said hurriedly, and leant forward to kiss Hillary. 'You're looking gorgeous,' she added warmly—but nervously? Hillary wondered in some confusion.

'I ... thank you,' she said a little bemusedly, and found herself also wondering if she was imagining the almost electric sparks of tension in the air. I feel like an actor in a play—the only one without a script ...

'Well, well!' a booming voice interrupted the oddly frozen little group they made—the Saunders, herself and her aunt, and the elderly gentleman Bea had been talking to who was beginning to look uncomfortable. It was Clarissa Hocking. 'So you all know each other, by the looks of it? Or do you? This is my new little protégée—she designed this room for me. Hasn't she got talent? Hillary, my dear, these are Irene and ...'

'Clarissa,' Charles interrupted mockingly, 'I hate to have to say this, but you're introducing our prospective daughter-in-law to us At least, I presume she is still that. I see you are wearing Ray's ring, Hillary. I must tell you, he was quite beside himself when you ... er ... disappeared like that.'

'Charles,' Irene whispered pleadingly.

But he was not to be stopped. 'I must admit, it crossed my mind to wonder if you'd popped off for a few days with your ... ex-husband perhaps? I see he's here as well tonight.'

Hillary closed her eyes briefly and the colour drained from her face leaving it unnaturally pale. And her aunt shut her mouth with a click, but before she could say anything, Clarissa intervened. 'Did you say ex-husband? Whose?'

Her words fell into a pool of silence, for it seemed as if the whole party had gone quiet and everyone was looking at them.

'Why, Hillary's,' Charles Saunders told her with a blandness that was totally menacing somehow. 'You're right, Clarrie, she's certainly a girl of many talents. Some that might surprise even you, though . . .'

There was a sudden movement and a sharp click. Hillary glanced sideways and saw that it was Clive. He had put his glass down. Their eyes locked, his faintly narrowed, and his mouth was set in a tight line.

Then he said, 'How you can put up with this idiot, Hillary, is beyond me. Do you really enjoy being either made a spectacle of or publicly humiliated?'

'Oh, I think it's more a case of she enjoys making a public spectacle of other people,' Charles said smoothly. 'My son, for one . . .'

'Stop it!' Hillary cried, her lips quivering and her eyes dark and shimmering with tears. 'Both of you . . . As for you,' she turned furiously to Charles, 'nothing *you* can say or do will have the slightest bearing on Ray and me!'

'As a matter of fact, I can vouch for that,' Clive drawled. 'You're going about this quite the wrong way, Mr Saunders, sir. What you don't understand is that the more opposition there is from you, the more determined Hillary will be to marry your precious son. It all goes back to what happened in *our* marriage, you see. Hillary is convinced I let her mother come between us, and I'd say she's vowed never to let herself be swayed similarly. Or am I wrong, Hillary?' he said directly to her, his grey eyes glinting ironically.

How ... She mouthed the word but didn't say it. How could you do this to me? Her eyes said it for her, though, and a nerve started to beat in Clive's jaw, but those hard grey eyes still probed her mercilessly.

Three things happened then almost simultaneously. Bea Selby said harshly, 'Now look here ...'; Hillary turned to flee; and Irene Saunders crumpled to the floor with a little moan of despair.

It was Martin Wessels, Hillary realised some minutes later, who got her out of the room and the house. He loomed up in the sudden confusion, placed one large hand on her elbow and, as the Red Sea might have parted for Moses, in the opposite direction to Clive people melted out of their path and he led her out on to the front veranda.

'Thank you so much,' she said, foolishly trying to smile through her tears. 'I can't imagine what you must think of me now ...'

'Don't,' he interrupted. 'Hillary,' he added abruptly, 'never care what people might think of you. That's the least of one's problems, believe me. You ... must have been very young when you married Clive.'

'She was,' Clive said right behind them. 'Too young to know any better. I'll take it from here, thanks, Martin.'

Oh no, you won't—oh no, you won't, Hillary

thought she was saying, but it was only in her head.
She was doing something though, walking, then
breaking out in to something faster, a stumbling run,
down the steps and along the front path.

But he caught her at the gate.

'Let me go, Clive!' She tried valiantly to free her
arm, but he said tersely, 'Stop it, Hillary. You'll
only get hurt.'

'That's something you seem to specialise in
doing to me, isn't it?' she panted, still struggling
furiously with tears of futility and misery
streaming down her face.

'Someone had to try and make you see the
truth,' he said grimly. 'Look, I don't want to hurt
you this way, but either you come quietly or that's
what will happen. Get in.'

They were standing opposite his car, and quite
how they'd got so far down the pavement, she
wasn't sure. But he had managed to unlock the
passenger door while he still had a hand clamped
round her wrist.

She stared up at him defiantly. 'No!'

'Then I'll put you in.'

'Clive . . .'

'I'm deadly serious, Hillary.'

His expression confirmed it and she looked
around despairingly, but it seemed everyone had
left her to her fate, incredibly.

She got into the car and he slipped into the
driver's seat beside her.

'I . . . I want to go home,' she stammered.

'When we've sorted a few things out,' he said
briefly, and started the car up.

She watched his impassive profile as he swung
the wheel, then, to her horror, she found herself
crying in earnest with her hands to her face and

great racking sobs tearing at her body.

He put an arm around her and she collapsed against him, unable to stop.

She never knew how he managed to drive, but it wasn't far to his house and, once there, he helped her out of the car and carried her inside as he'd done once before; but to the kitchen this time, where he sat her in one of the wooden chairs and reached for a bottle of brandy.

'Hillary,' he said gently, splashing some brandy into a glass, 'drink this. Come on, it will help.' He held the glass to her lips and she swallowed some of the brandy and choked and spluttered.

He sat down beside her and massaged her hands, then offered her some more, and this time it went down quite smoothly and that awful feeling of hysteria began to subside.

But in its place a sense of stark reality overtook her as she thought back to what Clive had said and further back, to herself and her inward reaction to Charles Saunders' malicious invective. Oh God, she thought, it did. It made me stiffen my spine and in a flash it cut through all my uncertainty, and if Ray had been there I'd have married him on the spot. No, that's ridiculous, but all the same, have I unwittingly made it a sort of personal crusade to marry Ray in spite of his parents because of what happened to me? Could I be so . . . criminally dense?

She looked up at last. 'Is that the truth, do you think?' she said tearfully to Clive.

CHAPTER EIGHT

CLIVE stared at her for a long time in silence. Then he stood up and poured himself a drink. 'Part of it, probably,' he said finally. 'You know, you've never wanted to tell me about Ray. But it occurred to me that he must be pretty . . . special, for you to willingly go through all that. Then, after the night we spent together,' he looked down at his drink, 'I wondered what it could be that was so special about him for you to . . . give yourself to another man so generously.' He twirled his glass absently.

'Clive,' she whispered, 'you're not just another man. I mean . . .' She stopped helplessly.

'All right.' He didn't look up. 'Have you told him?'

'I—haven't had the chance to. He's overseas.'

'But you plan to.' His lashes lifted suddenly.

'Yes . . .' She put a hand to her mouth.

'Think he'll understand? That he'll honestly not mind?'

Hillary took a tortured breath. 'He . . . he really loves me.'

'Hillary—don't you see, that's the other part of the problem. *You* see Ray as being in the position you were in—thought you were in—years ago. And you're determined not to do to him what I did to you. But that means, instead of a two-way thing, that you're in fact *assuming* responsibility for the fact that he loves you. Something I . . . well, you know what I did.' His lips twisted. 'But to make matters worse there's the double irony of his parental opposition. In a curious way it's like history repeating itself, only you've decided to ... change the course of history this time,' he said intently.

She stared at him with her lips parted. Then she said, 'All this is assuming that I don't really love him.'

He said carefully after a time, 'If you really loved him, don't you think you'd have loved to go to bed with him?'

'That's not *all* there is to ...'

'No,' he cut her short, 'of course it's not. But it's got to be part of it.'

'Like I did ... with you?' Her eyes were bleak.

'It's nothing to be ashamed of. But I can't help ... knowing it's a part of you. A special, wonderful part of you—and more, that it's something you've bestowed on no other lover. And that's why ... I can't believe you truly and passionately love Ray Saunders. That it's something ... less.'

'Are you trying to say ... it's because I can't forget you?'

He didn't answer for a time. Then he tossed off his drink and put the glass down on the table. 'I'd like to think that,' he said finally. 'But there's only one person who can be the judge of that. It could be,' he paused, then continued very levelly but with a hint of almost intolerable strain in his eyes, 'that there's a Mr Right somewhere out there for you, who ... combines some part of me and some part of Ray—brings it all together for you. If not, though, if it's because you can't forget me—well, I have to tell you I'm in the same boat.'

Hillary closed her eyes. 'Oh, Clive,' she murmured huskily. 'Don't *you* see—this is also like history repeating itself. Otherwise why now? Why not a year ago—two? The thing is, you're at a slack time of your life again.'

He made an abrupt movement, but she went on, 'And I'm—I suppose you could say I'm in a bit of a mess again.' She smiled faintly through her tears. 'That's when we appeal to each other, I think.'

'You weren't precisely in a mess when you first appealed to me,' he said harshly. 'I did that. I'm not trying to deny responsibility for it, Hillary, but . . .'

'It wasn't your fault I fell in love with you.'

He was silent for a time. Then he said ironically, 'I wish I could acquit myself of that. But about . . .'

'About being in a mess now?' she interrupted. 'I . . .' She took a shuddering breath, then said in a voice that was barely audible, 'I've been a fool about Ray. At least you've made me see that.'

'Hillary . . .' He looked suddenly tortured.

'No, you were right. The special things about him are all the wrong reasons to marry him. It would be like marrying a friend, a brother. And . . . you're right about the other part, too. I'm terribly afraid of hurting him, because I know how it can be. But in the long run I'd be hurting him more by marrying him, wouldn't I?'

He said nothing, just stared at her with his face a little drawn.

'And I think you're right—again,' she went on tremulously. 'What I really need is someone who will . . . bring it all together for me for all time. Not only the in-between times.' She saw him flinch through a haze of tears. 'But at least I've come to my senses,' she whispered.

He looked away.

'Clive . . .?'

He looked back at her at last. 'Yes,' he said gently, and smiled at her. 'What—what will you do?'

'Once I've told Ray?'

He nodded.

'Get back to work,' she said a little wryly. 'It seems to be the one area where I really know what I'm doing. And hope that Mr Right does come along one day, I guess.' The corners of her mouth trembled into a smile, but she couldn't quite hide the shadow of doubt in her eyes, which he saw, and he reached over and pulled her to her feet and took her into his arms.

'He will,' he said into her hair. 'Believe it. And I'll tell you how to know that he is—you won't even think about me, or Ray. That's one way you'll know.' His lips brushed her forehead and he held her very close. 'And that's when I'll know I'm forgiven.'

'You are, you are,' she whispered with her head against his heart. 'And one day it could happen for you, the same way.'

Clive lifted his head and stared down at her shining hair spilling across his sleeve. Then he closed his eyes and rested his cheek on her head. 'One day . . .' he said, but so softly she didn't catch the curious wryness with which he said it. 'I'll take you home now,' he added.

'Oh no! I forgot about her,' Hillary gasped. 'I mean, I thought she might have fainted, but . . . this.'

'We all thought that,' said Bea, looking oddly old and tired although she was still in her black silk dress and without a hair out of place. 'Then,' she shrugged, 'there was nothing you could have done. Besides,' she grimaced, 'you had problems of your own.'

'But will she be all right?' Hillary asked with white-faced distress.

'It's too early to say. With the heart . . .'

'I knew there was something . . . dreadfully wrong the minute I saw them. Saw Ray's mother anyway. She looked so old.'

'I thought that as well,' Bea agreed. 'Mind you, if there can ever be a good side to something like this, I wouldn't mind betting it forces Charles Saunders to examine some of his priorities. I don't mind telling you, Hillary, that I've formed the opinion, not altogether un-substantiated either, that he's put Irene through hell one way or another over the years. But he was absolutely distraught—you wouldn't have recognised him.'

'Oh God, I hope it's not too late! She . . . he . . . she really loves him,' Hillary whispered.

Bea was silent for a time. Then she said, 'You look exhausted yourself. What happened?'

Hillary looked down at her hands, at her beautiful blue suit which she knew with a sudden certainty she would never wear again. 'I came to my senses,' she said slowly.

'Because of what Clive said?'

Hillary nodded after a moment. 'I apologise for being so foolish,' she murmured. 'You tried to tell me, too, didn't you? Oh, not that bit precisely, but that I was marrying Ray for all the wrong reasons. I only wish I hadn't had to be hit over the head with it, publicly, to make me see it,' she said painfully. 'Especially now this has happened. She tried to tell me too—Irene. I didn't want to believe her either. It's strange though, she read me ... as accurately as you and Clive. In one way.'

They looked at each other and although Bea said nothing Hillary read the compassion and understanding in her aunt's eyes, and knew there was no need for words.

'But,' she said presently, 'this ... these two things happening at the same time is going to ... going to ...'

'Make it harder for Ray?' offered Bea. 'Possibly,' she said thoughtfully. 'And ... where does Clive stand now?'

'In the place I took years too long to put him.' Tears sparkled on Hillary's lashes but she went on resolutely. 'Of someone who did care what happened to me, and still does. But not the right person for me—either.'

'Does he ... agree?'

'Oh yes.' Hillary licked the salty tears from her lip. 'He said that some day Mr Right would come along for me.'

Bea Selby turned away sharply and Hillary frowned.

'What is it?' she queried.

'Nothing. Nothing—come to bed, my dear,' Bea said gently, turning back with only concern in her eyes.

Six months later, Hillary was walking through the City Mall on a bright summer's day when she stopped at a flower-seller and breathed in the heady scent of the masses of carnations. She closed her eyes and wondered why she felt like crying.

Then her eyes flew open as something was pushed into her hand and she gasped because it was a bunch of pink carnations and Ray was pressing them upon her.

'Ray . . . oh, Ray!'

'Hillary . . .'

She was in his arms then, laughing and crying a little, and the flower-seller retrieved the carnations from the cobbles, dusted them off, pushed them back into the bin and selected another bunch.

'Here you go, lady,' he said patiently.

'Oh! Oh, I'm sorry,' Hillary said guiltily. 'I got such a surprise.'

'Me, too,' said Ray. 'How about a cup of coffee?'

'I . . . think I might need one,' she answered tremulously.

'I can imagine why you were surprised,' Ray said, when they were seated in a dim, quiet little coffee shop. 'After the things I said to you all those months ago. I should have been shot.'

'Not you . . .'

'Yes, Hillary. But what with my mother's illness . . .'

'How is she?' Hillary interrupted.

'Fine. Although she'll always have to take things quietly. Most important of all—she's happy, as she hadn't been for a long time. So is my father, at last. It's as if he's found peace finally.'

'I'm so glad . . . And you?' Hillary said hesitantly. 'I read that you'd refused pre-selection for the by-election. Because of your mother?'

'Partly. But mostly because I decided I didn't want to be handed a blue-ribbon seat on a platter. When I stand, which will be at the next election, it will be in a seat where I have nothing going for me but myself.'

Hillary stirred her coffee with intense concentration because she was too moved to speak.

'And I have to thank you for making me see that that's the way it had to be, Hillary,' he said softly.

'Oh, Ray, you don't have to thank me for anything. After what I did to you ... So long as you don't hate and despise me any more ...'

He smiled. 'I could never hate you, Hillary. I know, I know. I said it all pretty forcefully. And for a long time I convinced myself I believed it. But wounded pride can be an ugly thing.'

'I know that,' she said shakenly. 'Is there,' she looked up, 'someone?'

'Yes ... It sprang out of nowhere.' He paused. 'It was the last thing I was looking for too,' he added wryly. 'Hillary,' his eyes searched her face, 'is there someone for you? At one stage I thought it might be Martin Wessels.'

'Oh, no. Well ... He rather thought he wanted it to be, but in the end we decided I was his lame duck. Anyway, most of the publicity was because of the film. No, there's no one. But,' she smiled back at him, 'I haven't given up hope that ... it will spring up out of nowhere for me, too. Only I'm so busy these days I could trip over it and never recognise it!'

'And—Clive Eastman?' Ray said quietly.

'Clive?' Hillary stared over Ray's shoulder and realised that for the second time in a matter of moments she'd seen the same girl walk past the coffee shop entrance in the arcade outside. She couldn't imagine why this girl should have caught her attention, except perhaps that she looked lost. About twenty, Hillary judged, and pretty but in a slightly uncoordinated way. As if it was something that came from within and she hadn't yet worked out how to help it along with clothes, etc. 'I haven't seen or heard anything about Clive for— well, since I last saw you. Round about then. I expect . . . He did say he was going to try his hand at conducting and I can imagine him being very good at that. I expect when we next hear about him, it will be in a blaze of glory.'

Ray started to say something, then bit his lip and looked at his watch instead. To start with surprise. 'Hell,' he said crossly, 'I'm supposed to be meeting someone. I was early when I saw you. Hillary . . .' He stopped awkwardly.

'Somewhere near here?' Hillary asked.

'As a matter of fact, yes. Well, just at the entrance to the arcade which is only . . .'

'A few yards away. Give her these, Ray,' Hillary said, and handed him the carnations. 'No, I want you to. I'm *so* happy for you—both. I'd like to her to have them,' she said with tears in her eyes. 'Go on!'

He stood up, then picked up the flowers and, stooping, kissed her on the forehead, and was gone.

They bumped into each other, right outside the coffee shop, Ray and the girl who had looked lost. Her quietly pretty face lit up and became beautiful as he took her into his arms. And a second bunch of carnations fell to the ground, but after a while she bent down and picked them up and buried her face in them . . .

'Some man rang for you,' Wendy said, that afternoon. 'Wouldn't leave his name. Said he'd try again. Hillary,' Wendy tapped her teeth with her pen, 'am I talking to myself? If so I'll go on. Since your name went up in lights . . .'

'It hasn't. Nor is it going to,' Hillary interposed absently. 'All that will happen will be that my name will flash briefly at the tail end of the titles.'

'Nevertheless, up to this point in time, there are no fewer than two film directors and three theatre companies vying for your services.'

'God knows why. All I did was rustle up some late nineteenth-century furniture.'

'Mr Wessels,' Wendy said severely, 'thought you had great talent as a set designer. He told me so. I'd say he's been spreading the word. But to get back to the man who rang . . .'

'I thought we'd disposed of him—lost him in the course of this monologue,' Hillary teased.

'Not at all,' Wendy replied placidly. 'He's the central figure.'

'What do you mean?'

'He was a Pom,' said Wendy with the air of pulling a rabbit out of a hat.

'So?'

'A very posh-sounding Pom!'

'Well?'

'I think he might also be after your services. It could even have been Richard Attenborough or . . .'

'Wendy!' Hillary protested laughingly. 'I can assure you it wouldn't have been!'

'That's better,' Wendy said complacently.

'What . . . what do you mean?' asked Hillary, still grinning.

'Thought you looked a bit down in the dumps. Thought I'd try and make you laugh. Something happen today?' Wendy enquired delicately.

Hillary put the sheaf of papers she had in her

hand down and grimaced. 'In a way. I bumped into Ray.'

'Want to tell me about it?'

Hillary did, briefly. 'Actually I'm very happy for him, and intensely relieved. She looked—just right for him. So I'm really not down in the dumps at all,' she added brightly.

Could have fooled me, Wendy thought, and sighed inwardly; but as was her habit, although she would willingly have died for Hillary she sometimes thought, she didn't pursue the matter.

'By the way,'' said Hillary, looking at the time, 'didn't you want to get off half an hour earlier today? I thought Len was taking you down the coast for the long weekend and you wanted to beat the traffic?'

'Well, yes,' Wendy said slowly.

'What's this? Having second thoughts about Len?'

Wendy's face softened. 'No,' she said. 'Although I probably should. When love comes to one this late in life,' she murmured a little ruefully, 'you tend to be a bit cynical about it. But I've worked out that he can't be after my money because I haven't got that much, he can't be solely after my body because, it could be said, I have more than enough in that line, so it must be me, body *and* soul.'

'Wendy,' Hillary said softly, 'I've seen him looking at you when he thinks no one is watching and if he's not a man deeply in love, I'll eat my hat!'

'Do you . . . really think so?' Wendy's voice was uncharacteristically shaky.

'*Yes*. Now off you go. And have fun. Because you're a person in a million and you deserve it.'

'Here,' smiled Wendy, dabbing at her eyes, 'I think I will. Before I get all emotional. See you Tuesday, love,' she said, and pressed Hillary's hand. Then she was gone.

Hillary moved quietly around the shop tidying up and found it curiously soothing. These days she didn't get to spend much time in it at all and sometimes regretted it.

Then she made herself a cup of coffee and took it to the counter, but instead of spending the last ten minutes before closing up checking the takings, she sat with her elbows on the counter and her chin in her hands, staring at a last ray of sunlight coming through the window to illuminate an old brass kettle so that it looked as if it was made of pure gold.

And she found herself thinking again of Ray and how true what she had said to Wendy was. She was intensely relieved, because she had borne a burden of almost intolerable guilt over the past six months. Not only for what she had done to him when she had told him she couldn't marry him but also because of what he had revealed in that bitter, hurting confrontation.

When she had disappeared for those three days, to Noosa, Ray had turned on both his mother and father and accused them of having found some new way to break up their engagement. His mother had broken down and told him she had been to see Hillary, and what she had said, and the ensuing row had, as often happens, mushroomed. To the extent that Ray had found himself accusing his father, in front of his mother, of being a lecher and, if that wasn't despicable enough, a self-righteous hypocrite; it seemed he had known for a long time of his father's extra-marital activities.

And for months after, Hillary had been haunted, not only by Ray's agony but by Irene Saunders' face on the last night she had seen her.

'What do they say?' she murmured, coming back to the present with a shiver. 'All's well that ends well. How trite! I mean, I'm glad it's ended well, but can you ever totally forgive yourself?'

She blinked and realised that the ray of sunlight had faded and the kettle was back to brass. And I've got a long weekend in front of me, she reflected, and nowhere to go and nothing to do. Nothing that I really feel like doing anyway. I wish Aunt Bea was back.

But her aunt was with a party of friends, sampling the wines of the Barossa Valley. Everyone's with someone except me, she thought wryly, and jumped as the someone came into the shop.

Hillary peered through the half gloom at the figure of a man and thought she must be imagining things.

Then she said, 'Why, Ned—I mean, Mr Cartwright, is it really you?'

'None other,' Ned Cartwright replied with a chuckle. 'But please call me Ned.'

'Oh,' Hillary laughed a little embarrassedly, 'I didn't mean to be rude. But I've always thought of you as Ned since the day I once started to ... write a letter to you for Clive ...' She trailed off awkwardly.

'Telling me I was fired, no doubt?'

'Well ... But he changed his mind. Did you ... Is this ... I mean, did you come in to buy something?' She stood up.

'I came to see you, my dear,' Ned Cartwright said. 'We very nearly got to meet each other once,

but I didn't expect you to recognise me. I rang
earlier, by the way.'

'Oh! It was you ... There's nothing ... Has
something happened to ...' She couldn't finish
and realised her heart was beating like a drum.

'No! Clive's fine, Hillary. May I call you that?
Actually, I was wondering if you'd have dinner
with me tonight. It's my last night in Australia.'

'Well, yes, but ...'

'Fine,' said Ned Cartwright. 'I've got a taxi
waiting outside for me and an appointment in
fifteen minutes, and if you didn't think it was
extremely discourteous of me, I was wondering if
you'd care to meet me in the restaurant of my
hotel,' he named it, 'say at ... eight o'clock?'

'Yes. No. I mean I don't think it's discourteous,'
Hillary said dazedly.

'Well, I shall be looking forward to it very
much,' Ned said, and left as quietly as he'd come.

Hillary stared at herself in the mirror and frowned
slightly. She was wearing a simple linen dress in a
dusky pink that, together with a lavender blue,
wide soft belt and matching shoes, was certainly
elegant enough to be seen in, taking dinner at the
hotel where she had once worked.

But it had suddenly dawned on her that the
weight she had lost in her figure was beginning to
show in her face, too. And not only that. There
seemed to be permanent faintly violet shadows
beneath her eyes. All of which, she knew, bore
testimony to a hard half year in more ways than
one. She had worked like a dog, too, and not only
on Martin Wessels' film but more and more on
interior decorating projects.

'I need a holiday,' she murmured. 'And now

that I've had Ray's news to ... set my mind at peace, this might be the time to take it.'

She reached for her slim, dusky pink suede handbag and noticed that her fingers were a little unsteady, and she forced herself to take a deep breath and relax.

But why me? she asked her reflection. Why does Ned Cartwright want to have dinner with me? It has to be something to do with Clive because that's the only point of reference between us. And that being so, should I be doing this?

This thing is, you've left it a little late to back out now, Hillary, haven't you?

Yes ...

'It's a curious thing,' said Ned. 'I'm not a great traveller, you know. But this is the second time I've been to Australia in the space of a year now. I really find it fascinating. How is your duck?'

'Delicious,' Hillary said. 'Then—you're only out here on a holiday?'

'Yes. Well, mostly. And it's been magical. I've seen the Great Barrier Reef, Ayers Rock, the outback ...' He went on describing his holiday to her while Hillary tried to pretend that she was hungry when in fact she was wading through her duck with no appetite at all. Which isn't his fault, she thought. He's done his best to put me at my ease and despite ... What did Martin say about him that night? Such a dry-looking little man ... Despite that, he's really rather sweet. And he has the wisest eyes I think I've ever seen. All the same, why did he want to have dinner with me?

'My dear,' Ned's voice broke into her thoughts abruptly, 'I'm afraid I've been a little foolish. Leave that duck—I can see it's becoming a monumental task to finish it. Here, let me top up your wine. You're wondering, I'm sure, what this is all about?'

Hillary nodded after a moment and put her knife and fork down relievedly. 'I'm sorry,' she murmured unhappily.

'Don't be. I really wanted to meet you. And I wanted to talk to you about Clive. Do you mind?'

'I ... I ...' Hillary whispered. 'I don't know. Has ... he asked you to?'

'No! He has no idea.'

'Then what did you want to talk to me about?'

'He's ... getting married.'

The world seemed to tilt sideways, but just as Hillary confidently expected everything on the table to start to slide off, it righted itself and she heard the muted babble of voices again and the soft sound of the piano playing in the background and the chink of crockery.

She swallowed. 'That's great news.'

Ned Cartwright studied her keenly but said nothing for a moment.

Hillary licked her lips. 'How ... how's his music going?'

'He's given it up completely—professionally, that is.'

'*What!*' Her voice was hoarse with disbelief.

'Strangely enough,' said Ned, 'I think he's made the right decision. Whatever else he did in that field would only be second best for him. Clive was a genius, I believe. Perhaps the best I've heard on some occasions. He could express himself on a violin so that it got into your soul. I think he's realised that it was his special area and to pursue another form of it would only be frustrating. He's one of those all-or-nothing kind of people.'

'But what will he do?' Hillary asked, as she'd done once before.

'Well, he's nothing if not resourceful,' Ned said a trifle drily. 'As a matter of fact I think it was one of his early torments, that he could turn his hand to so many things. For one thing, he's bought a farm near Beaudesert and plans to breed and race horses. For another, he's writing a book, an autobiography, which from what I've seen of it, and if I'm any judge, could become a bestseller. Because he's handling it with a great deal of humour as well as some quite punishing insights into the kind of egotism that so often drives a virtuoso of any description. All the same, I don't suppose he's having an easy time of it, exactly.'

Hillary shivered and found herself picturing, with the utmost clarity, a broken violin . . .

'And who is he marrying?' she asked very quietly.

'An exceptionally beautiful young lady—that goes without saying.' Ned's eyes twinkled briefly. 'She's part of the landed gentry of the area, the daughter, in fact, of the property next door to the one he's bought.' He paused. 'I found her . . . beneath that beautiful and undoubtedly intelligent exterior, I thought she was just a little hard.'

Hillary blinked. 'She might need to be,' she whispered. 'Why . . . why did you want to tell me this?'

'I gather Clive was instrumental in helping you to avoid an unsuitable marriage, Hillary,' Ned said gently.

Hillary stared at him, her eyes shocked and incredulous. 'You're not suggesting I do the same for him?'

Ned shrugged. 'Why not? I happen to know that you two mean a great deal to each other.'

'No . . .'

'You don't?' he enquired, with his head cocked alertly to one side.

'I mean—I couldn't do it. This is different.'

'In what way?'

Hillary closed her eyes and summoned every ounce of rational thought at her disposal. 'For one thing—forgive me, but what makes you think this is an unsuitable marriage for him? Just because you . . . didn't altogether like her?'

'My dear Hillary, no.' Ned sat back and pursed his lips. 'Perhaps,' he said then, 'I should explain some things to you. What I am, commonly called an agent, is a term that covers a vast range of things. You generally become closer to your artistes than anyone else, wives, mothers, the lot. You become their . . . punching bags, their confessors and a whole lot else besides. And sometimes you become genuinely fond of your . . . *enfant terrible*.' He smiled slightly. 'I was that long before this happened to Clive. I will always hold him in great esteem and affection despite the fact that he can be most . . . difficult at times. And now, I have a new respect for him for the way he's coping with this disaster.' He paused and sipped his wine. 'I'm telling you all this for two reasons, Hillary,' he went on. 'In the hope that you might understand why I've taken the liberty of intruding, as well.'

'Well . . .'

Ned held up a hand. 'Let me finish, please. For example, I think I'm probably the only person in whom Clive finally confided about you.'

Hillary moved abruptly.

Ned went on undeterred. 'When he came back to Europe six years ago, he was like a man possessed by the devil. He lived hard—harder than usual; his playing was brilliant, yet it bordered on . . . it's hard to describe, but there was a touch of evil genius about it. And he not only played as if he was tormented, he looked it, too. Then, finally, when I thought he was going to have a nervous breakdown, I taxed him with it. Boldly. I said to him, Clive, have you killed someone? Have you committed a murder? Because you're beginning to look as if you're pursued by all the guilt in hell.'

Hillary held her breath and again it was as if something had happened to the world.

'He didn't answer for a long time,' Ned said. 'Then he looked at me. And he said, yes. Who? I asked, considerably taken aback as you can imagine, since my question had only been intended to shock him. He replied, innocence, faith, purity—I killed them all.'

Hillary made an inarticulate little sound and spilt some of her wine on the tablecloth.

Ned swiftly placed his napkin over the golden stain and poured her some more. 'Drink it,' he said gently but imperatively.

She did as she was bid and some colour came back to her cheeks gradually. 'I know now,' she whispered, 'that he really regretted what happened. I do know it . . .'

'But I wonder if you know what else he said to me? After I'd almost forcibly made him explain, he said, if only one could turn back the clock. If only I could wipe it all out and meet her again when she's grown up properly, when she's more sure of herself, when she's not so defenceless—you know what I'm like, Ned. Because, he said then, I'm very much afraid I might have killed my heart as well . . .'

'Are you . . . what are you trying to say?' Hillary asked with her eyes dark.

Ned drew a deep breath, 'I'm trying to make it known to you, Hillary, that you touched something within Clive Eastman that no one else has ever touched. Something that this girl has no *hope* of reaching . . . In fact, I think that's why he's marrying her, part of it. His talent for being an evil genius hasn't altogether deserted him, I'm afraid.'

'I . . . I don't understand,' Hillary stammered.

Ned looked at her compassionately. 'When Clive came back here,' he said, 'I think he confirmed something to himself. That he'd always loved you and always would. But that he couldn't turn back the clock because the injury he'd done you was too great. All the same, I think he might have tried?' He looked at her with his eyebrows raised.

'He . . . but really only to stop me from marrying Ray, I think,' she said unsteadily. 'And because he was—bereft.'

'Exactly,' said Ned.

'I . . .' She looked at him bewilderedly.

'If you could put yourself in his place, wouldn't you be inclined to wonder whether any response *you* might have made was dictated by—pity, perhaps?'

Hillary caught her breath. 'I still don't see . . .'

'What it has to do with this marriage? I think it's quite simple. I don't think he trusts himself not to try again. I think he's trying to put as much space between the two of you as he possibly can.'

'But that's diabolical! I mean, the poor girl . . .' Hillary stopped abruptly and stared at Ned helplessly.

'I've never denied that Clive can be diabolical when he sets his mind to it. However, I suspect she can more than fend for herself. But we do do strange things at times, don't we, Hillary, all of us?' Ned said intently. 'Or was Clive wrong to interfere in *your* marriage plans?'

Hillary put a hand to her mouth. 'No,' she said after a long time.

He sat back. 'Of course,' he said gently, 'all this is academic if you really find you can't forgive him, can't live with him, are better off, happier without him.'

'W-what if you're wrong . . .?'

He smiled wisely. 'I'm not. But it's easy enough to prove, isn't it? Just go and ask him. Oh, I'm not suggesting you do it in the spectacular manner he did—on the other hand, why not? Some of his own medicine might be what he needs.'

'I . . . I couldn't!' Hillary protested, her face flushed now and her hands unsteady again. 'You may know Clive, but how can you be so sure about her? Maybe she really loves him?'

'Hillary—and I spent a week with them—I sincerely believe she's the kind of person who loves nobody better than herself. And in that respect, perhaps we were a little hard on Clive earlier. I think he knows it.'

'Are they . . . are they living together?'

'More or less.'

More or less. More than less—no, he didn't say that. But how could I do it? Clive, I've come to . . . interfere in your marriage plans! I've come to check your fiancée out, see if she's a suitable wife for you . . . Why? Why not? You did no less for me . . .

Hillary pushed aside her tangled sheets and got up to wander restlessly over to the window. It was a stifling night with the humidity so high she was covered in a thin film of sweat, although her ceiling fan was on and clicking madly at full speed. And the window was wide open and the curtains drawn back, but there was no hint of movement in the air. Nor was there any moonlight left, so it was a dark, shapeless outlook she gazed upon.

'Anyway,' she murmured, 'if I were to appoint a suitable wife for you, Clive, what would she be like? Apart from her not being like me, the choice could be limitless. It's not as if you suffer from the kind of hang-ups I did . . . A little hard? Well, as I said to Ned, she might need to be, only . . . Was he right? Ned, I mean,' she said conversationally to the darkened landscape. 'He could be only guessing, he *must* be to an extent. All the same, he didn't strike me as the kind of person who would . . . gamble on an uninformed guess. The thing is, what would I be gambling on if I did as he suggested? It's all over and done with now, it has to be, so I could only be . . . creating an extremely awkward situation, perhaps. Unless . . .'

She pulled her nightgown away from her body and tried to fan herself with it. 'No,' she said with sudden decision. 'No. It would be madness.'

CHAPTER NINE

A PAIR of exquisite green eyes regarded Hillary lazily.

'I ... wonder if I could see Mr Eastman, please?' asked Hillary, stammering in her nervousness, but not only that, in her conviction that she had lapsed into insanity from the moment she had steered her car in the direction of the Beaudesert Shire this lovely Sunday morning.

'He's out,' the girl in the doorway said abruptly, straightening to reveal a lovely figure that not even the jodhpurs and loose shirt she wore could disguise. And she flicked her red-gold hair back as she added, 'Something important? Perhaps I can help. I'm his fiancée.'

'I ... Will he be long?' Hillary rubbed her hands together awkwardly.

'Shouldn't think so. We're expecting twelve people for lunch in about an hour's time. Although if I know Clive he'll only get back at the last minute. You can wait if you like,' the girl said indifferently. 'If it's that important.'

'Oh no,' Hillary said on a breath. 'I'm afraid I've chosen my time rather badly. And it's nothing important really.'

A faint frown came to those green eyes. 'Then why the mystery bit?' she demanded of Hillary with sudden hauteur.

'There ... there's no mystery,' Hillary said with an effort.

'Could have fooled me. And why are you so

uptight?' There was more than a hint of a frown now in the way she was looking at Hillary.

Oh God! Hillary cried inwardly, and couldn't have been more surprised at the manner of divine intervention she invoked—it had to be that, she thought later, a great flash of inspiration which led me to reel off a whole tissue of lies so glibly. Or is it the devil who helps one to lie so convincingly?

'I ... am a little embarrassed. I ... have a child who plays the violin, you see. She's very good—well, I—we think so. And I was wondering if Mr Eastman would perhaps be able to spare just a very little time to ... to hear her. Of course I realise it's a great imposition, but ...' She stopped as the redheaded girl—Clive's future *wife*, she reminded herself—burst into a peal of clear, high laughter.

'Well, I doubt it,' the girl said finally. 'He's given all that up.'

'He has?' Hillary managed to look totally shocked.

'Uh-huh.'

'Oh, I'm so sorry! I ... I'll go now. Do forgive me for this.'

'All right.' It was quite obligingly said. 'You weren't to know. 'Bye now!'

''Bye.'

How she managed to drive home was something of a miracle to Hillary. Because, what with castigating herself for having ever taken any notice of Ned Cartwright's advice, and getting lost in the dusty gold backblocks of the Beaudesert Shire, with its beautiful old homesteads such as Clive's had been, set amidst their acres of ground, and hating herself for ever thinking she had the right to interfere—it *was* something of a miracle she made it home.

But once home, she was seized by a desire to be gone again. Because after all, home was the place she'd spent the last two days agonising over what Ned had told her, home was the place where she'd made the mad decision to go and see Clive, home was the place where she'd unearthed a map and traced a route out of Brisbane to the address Ned had given her.

Home was the loneliest place on earth—was that why she'd succumbed? she wondered torturedly.

Well, I can do something about that, she answered herself in the next breath. Instead of dreaming about a holiday, I can take one right now. All I have to do is pack and leave a couple of notes. Wendy can hold the fort for me and I'll probably be back before Aunt Bea gets home anyway.

An hour or so later, just as the sun was setting, she was ready. Noosa again? she wondered as she put her case down in the hall and rifled through her handbag for her car keys. No . . .

She jumped then as, just as she put her hand on the doorknob, someone rapped on it from outside. She forced herself to take a steadying breath. It can't possibly be . . . No, she told herself, and opened the door.

But it was.

'Clive!' she gasped.

He said nothing for a moment, just stood there looking tall and formidable in his jeans and suede jacket.

Then he murmured, 'Hello, Hillary. I've come to listen to this . . . child of yours who plays the violin.'

'It wasn't me . . .' The words were out before she could stop them and she turned instantly scarlet, as if what she'd said hadn't been enough of a give-away. And in an agony of despair, she tried to slam the door on him, but after a sharp, angry struggle, he was not only inside, but he'd picked her up and carried her into the lounge and deposited her in a chair.

'You're lying,' he gritted through his teeth, as he imprisoned her in the chair with his hands on both arms. 'I want to know why.'

She licked her lips. 'How . . .?'

He gazed down at her white face, at the shadows like faint bruises beneath her eyes, and straightened abruptly. 'How did I know it was you? Stacey described you. In fact, she did more. She turned your visit into a lunchtime anecdote—such an amusing thing happened this morning, she said. This woman turned up, Clive, and for a moment or two I quite thought it was one of your ex-mistresses . . .'

Hillary closed her eyes.

'Naturally,' he said ironically, 'I pricked up my ears and wanted to know more—despite the fact that I haven't had a mistress for some time. Stacey is never one to . . . miss an opportunity to prove how sophisticated she is, or what a good raconteuse for that matter, so she pushed the story to its limit. She described you feature by feature, also how . . . desperately anxious were the words she used, you looked. Then, when she had us all breathless, she pulled out the punch line about the kid who played the violin. Everyone thought it was hilarious,' he said grimly. 'Everyone except me, that is. Because I was wondering if it was an amazing coincidence—was there someone in the area who fitted your description exactly? Someone with straight fairish hair and a heart-shaped face and smoky-blue eyes, someone not very tall and in her mid-twenties—who even drove an identical car?'

Hillary made an inarticulate sound.

'Oh, she got it all, Stacey did. She's very perceptive in some ways. And she has an instinct for some things. The right instinct in this case.'

They stared at each other. 'Do you mean . . . she didn't believe me?' Hillary whispered at last.

'Quite possibly she has some doubts,' he said drily. 'I haven't discussed it with her. We . . . left it at that.'

She buried her face in her hands and the minutes ticked by.

'Why did you come?' he said at last.

Hillary tried to speak several times, but when it became obvious she couldn't, Clive lifted her to her feet and held her in a savage embrace. 'Look at me,' he said roughly. 'And start talking. Are you in some kind of trouble?'

'No . . . no.'

'Then what have you been doing to yourself? I could pick you up with one hand! Don't tell me you've been pining for Ray bloody Saunders!' He put a hard hand beneath her chin and forced her to look up. 'You stupid little fool,' his grey eyes glittered menacingly, 'he was never the right one for you. I thought we'd sorted that out!'

A spark of anger lit Hillary's eyes. 'I wasn't pining for him,' she said huskily. 'But I just can't dismiss people as easily as you can,' she added contemptuously.

His mouth tightened. 'As easily as I dismissed you, do you mean?'

'No!'

'Oh, I think you do,' he said silkily. 'In fact I think you're more like your mother than you ever dreamt, Hillary. You just can't forgive, can you? Is that what happened today?' he asked, overriding her shocked protest as well as her futile struggle to free herself. 'Did you—God knows why you came in the first place—but did you get a shock to discover yourself confronted with my fiancée? Such a shock that you lied in your teeth. Is that what happened?'

'I already knew . . .' She stopped abruptly.

He put her a little away from him and stared at her with his eyes narrowed. 'Did you now,' he said finally. 'Well! The plot thickens. You know, you're going to have to explain, my dear.'

'Let me go, Clive,' she whispered, white to the lips.

'All right,' he said after a moment, and released her. 'But I'm not leaving here until you do,' he said casually, and he took his coat off and strolled over to her cocktail cabinet and poured himself a neat Scotch, which he tossed off and then poured himself another. 'Like one?' he queried, and without waiting for an answer poured another and brought it over to her and put it into her hand. 'Sit down,' he said genially, and did so himself.

A living tide of white-hot fury welled up within Hillary. 'I hate you, Clive!' she cried, dashing the Scotch on to the carpet. 'And I was so wrong. I came up to see y-you,' her voice shook, 'because I thought you might be the one making a mistake this time. But I'm sure you're not at all. I'm sure you know exactly what you're doing and I'm glad you're doing it! Do you hear? Glad . . .' Her voice sank on the last word and she gritted her teeth and stared down at the empty glass in her hands wanting to smash it, to do something, anything that was violent and destructive, anything that would ease the dreadful turmoil of her mind ...

She lifted her head at last to find that Clive was staring at her with something very much like disbelief in his eyes.

Then he put his glass down carefully and stood up and came over to her.

She swallowed and backed away a step. But he did nothing, just stood there. 'Did you say you thought I might be the one making a mistake this time?' His voice was low and a little unsteady. 'Why?'

'I ... wondered if she was the right one for you,' whispered Hillary, her rage leaving her as suddenly as it had come, leaving her desperate for the right words to say and on the verge of tears. She blinked and tried to smile. 'I know it was foolish because—well, I'm sure you're not as stupid as I can be ... was. You were right about Ray. He's found someone else who really loves him, I think ...'

Her articulateness, if it could be called that, deserted her then and, after a few false starts, she went to turn away, but he spoke at last. 'How did you know?'

'It doesn't matter ...'

'Then why,' he said with an effort, 'did you get cold feet?'

'I *told* you ...'

'Does that mean you don't really care? That you're more afraid of making a fool of yourself?'

Hillary licked her lips. 'I do care...' She swallowed. 'Oh, Clive,' she said with sudden intensity then, 'it's not only that. I've caused

enough people so much pain with my ...
blunderings around. If you only knew!'

'I do. But you can't blame yourself for what
happened to Mrs Saunders, Hillary.'

'All the same, it's hard not to ... How did you
know about her?'

'My old mate Clarissa kept me updated,' he
explained. 'From her point of view, I doubt if she's
ever given a more sensational birthday party.'

Hillary shivered and he put out a hand, but
when she moved sharply away, he let it drop to his
side.

'All right,' he said in a different voice, 'shall we
just put what you did today ... down to an
impulse?'

'A foolish one,' she said tremulously—and
added more steadily, 'As a matter of fact, I
thought ... Stacey was very lovely and ...
spirited, and you have my blessing.'

Something flickered in his eyes that she couldn't
decipher. But he said only, 'Thank you. Will you
do one thing for me?'

'What?'

He gazed at her. 'Take a holiday or something.
You look as if you could do with it.'

'Funny you should say that! I was just on my
way when you arrived ...'

Two minutes later she was staring at the closed
door with her hand to her mouth where he'd
kissed her lips lightly. And she made no move for
a long time, just stared at the door with a dawning
look of horror in her eyes.

Why now? she wondered numbly, why do I
know now, with utter *certainty*, that I love him in
every way it's possible to love a man? Even if he is
impossible, even with his talent for ... evil genius,

even after what he did to me ... What's finally
unlocked this secret? Is it because I can't have him?
Or because I did nearly become more like my mother
than I ever dreamt? Unable to forgive ... Or was it
you, Ned? What you said, rather, that made me hope
he might truly love me? I'd never dared to believe it
before, not really. But you see, you were wrong and I
was right all along—about Clive. Just wrong about
myself. You poor fool, Hillary, she marvelled.

'You poor fool!' Bea Selby said witheringly, and
because those words seemed to have burnt
themselves into Hillary's brain, although it was
nearly three months since she'd said them out loud
to herself, she winced from sheer habit, then
looked at her aunt enquiringly.

'Who?'

'This silly woman.' Bea rustled the Sunday
paper impatiently.

'What silly woman?'

'The one ... oh, it doesn't matter. She's so
tangled up with husbands and lovers— It's a great
source of concern to me, Hillary, that whatever
you do for them, women on the whole are like a
lot of sheep. In fact it's worse, they remind me of
the Labour Party!' Bea said haughtily.

Hillary grinned and didn't even attempt to
clarify the cross-references in this speech.

'Which reminds me,' her aunt continued, glaring
suddenly at her niece instead of the paper. 'What's
happened to you lately? Why do you look as if
you've reached some hidden nirvana? Not that I'm
not happy to see you looking better—I just can't
work out the reason for it!'

'It could be that I've shed myself of husbands
and lovers,' Hillary said tranquilly.

'I have never,' Bea pronounced chillingly, 'denied their value—in an orderly sequence. I do deplore it when you get to the stage,' she flicked the paper with a finger, 'of not knowing who is the father of your child and end up subjecting us all to the sordidness of paternity suits. Besides which, you've never had a lover in your life. Only a husband. So don't sit there being smug.'

'I'm not. And I'm not going out to get a lover just to please you, Aunt Bea. Does that make me a candidate for the Labour Party?'

'Hillary,' Bea said abruptly.

'It's all right, Aunt Bea,' Hillary murmured. 'Really it is.'

Her aunt regarded her searchingly, but Hillary only continued to look amused.

Bea sighed inwardly and picked up the paper again—to say, not very long aftwards, 'Well!'

'What's it this time?'

'It's—oh, nothing,' her aunt murmured, and glanced at her watch. 'Good Lord, I'll be late for lunch if I'm not careful!' And she folded the paper and placed it on the coffee table. 'Doing anything yourself?' she asked Hillary.

'Yes. Washing my hair, my underclothes, giving myself a manicure—all the things you do on Sundays,' Hillary replied, and added, 'when you're a working girl,' fully expecting her aunt to take issue with her, but for once in her life, Bea surprised her.

She came over to her and kissed her cheek. 'See you later then, love,' she said gently. 'I'll be back for dinner, probably.'

Now I wonder what that was all about? Hillary mused. Only to discover a couple of hours later what had caused her aunt's change of mood . . .

She had washed her hair and decided to dry it in the sun, and she picked up the paper Bea had left folded on the coffee table to take out on to the veranda with her.

But as she sat down a face seemed to leap out at her and, with startled eyes, she began to read the caption to the photo. Stacey Thornton-Smith, it said, pictured above and well-known in riding circles, has announced her engagement to Bradley Summers. This marriage will bring together not only two notable families of the Beaudesert Shire, but also two top competitors in the equestrian field.

Hillary closed her eyes and let the paper drop. Because it was as if a gaping chasm had opened up at her feet—the same one she'd pulled herself out of not so very long ago ...

'No, don't do this to me,' she whispered with silent tears rolling down her cheeks. 'I've come to terms with it, I've learned to live with it ... For a time I felt like dying, but I clawed my way back and built another wall—is that all it was? I was so sure I'd achieved peace at last, but this ... more than proves that, even if she wasn't the right one for him, I'm not either or he would have come ...'

She buried her face in her hands and wept into them, her hair still damp and springy and glinting in the sunlight as it fell awry over her hands.

She couldn't say what it was that impinged on her grief, but all of a sudden she looked up, to see Clive standing a few feet away.

For a heart-stopping moment, she couldn't believe her eyes, then she took a gulping breath and climbed to her feet, only to be able to stand beside her chair defensively, although she wanted to run for her life. And the paper lay on the floor between them with Stacey staring upwards . . .

Her eyes were drawn to the picture like a magnet and he followed her gaze, but looked up immediately.

He knows, she thought chaotically, and felt her cheeks begin to burn. Caught red-handed . . . 'You mustn't feel sorry for me,' she heard herself saying, as she pressed her palms together. 'I . . . It's not what you think, really. I mean, you must be feeling very sad. She was . . . she was so lovely . . .' What am I trying to say? she wondered frantically.

'She also broke off *our* engagement of her own free will, Hillary,' he said. 'It wasn't anything I did other than being myself, so much as that she came to realise that she'd loved Brad for a long time. They were childhood friends, you see, but sometimes . . . familiarity tends to cloud the view. I was, for her, a sort of sampling of the field, in a way. Not intentionally, perhaps, but that's the way it worked out. She's very happy, now.'

'Why . . . why are you telling me this?' Hillary stammered.

He said, 'In the hope that, now I can prove to you that *no one* will be hurt if you and I get married again, you . . . will say yes. I did understand one thing you said to me the last time we met—that it would be useless to tell you and try to persuade you that I loved you and always had while there was still Stacey. I also understood that I couldn't just cast her off, that you'd never feel right about it and neither would I.' He sketched a smile that didn't reach his eyes. 'I might finally be learning that one has to pay for one's thoughtless actions—belatedly. Is . . . that what you were trying to say to me, Hillary?' His grey eyes were suddenly very acute. 'Was I right?'

She put her hands to her heart and her lips formed his name, but no sound came.

'If,' he said with an effort, 'you're wondering why I wanted to marry her in the first place, I can tell you that, too. To stop myself from ever hurting you again. I know,' he said, as her eyes widened, 'it was a lousy thing to do to anyone, but I guess you of all people must know how . . . extra capable I am of these things. But it seemed to me, in a moment of bleakness and despair at the thought that I'd killed everything you ever felt for me . . . it seemed like a good idea.'

'You didn't . . .'

'Well, not quite everything,' he interrupted. 'You proved that there was still . . . understanding left, compassion, and that's how I thought I could go on hurting you, you see. And myself,' he said barely audibly, and looked away briefly. 'Myself, by trying to read more into it than it was; you, by trying to persuade you it was more than it was. Then you came up to the farm and I thought, I wondered . . . I began to hope again. Only to realise, that same night, that whatever the reason you'd come, it was too late for me because I'd made it too late, single-handedly. That you couldn't live with Stacey on your conscience, as you thought of it, too.'

'Oh, Clive,' she whispered, her heart beating erratically and her lips trembling.

'Hillary,' his grey eyes were shadowed and his voice uneven, 'there's still no reason—I mean, none of this is any reason for you to say yes to me now, unless . . . you love me. It's my affair that I found out so many things too late. And just about anyone in their right mind would tell you to keep clear of me, but if . . .'

'If I love you?' she said shakily and found she was crying again. 'I never stopped . . .'

'Oh God,' he said torturedly. 'I'll probably never change in some ways.'

'I know.'

'In fact it could be worse now. I still get horribly frustrated sometimes—you know what it's like . . .'

'Yes, but I've grown up. And I've got a career now which I can keep on with. I . . . it's something that makes me—well, sure of myself, and that's what I lacked desperately before. I also know now that I could only ever love *you*.'

'After all I did to you . . .'

'Clive,' she smiled through her tears, 'did you come to ask me to marry you again or talk me out of it? I'll never marry anyone else, you know.'

His left eyebrow shot up. 'Oh well, in that case,' he said softly, 'if you honestly and truly . . .'

'I do,' she whispered, and went into his arms.

The shadows were lengthening outside when Hillary stirred and murmured something drowsily.

'What's that?' Clive asked against the satiny skin of her bare shoulder.

She came fully awake with a jolt, then started to smile. 'I was dreaming of you,' she murmured. 'I wonder why?'

'Something to do with what happened before you went to sleep?' he said, and started to kiss the hollows at the base of her throat.

Hillary tilted her head back in sheer pleasure. 'Probably . . .'

'You know,' he lifted his head, 'I could spend my life doing this.'

'So could I,' she whispered.

Clive laughed softly. 'Seriously,' he said a

moment later, and pulled another pillow behind her head so that she was half-sitting up, naked to the waist where the sheet lay, with the glow of the sunset that filled the room gilding her breasts and her hair, 'perhaps we should pace ourselves.'

'Why?' She lifted a hand and touched his hair, then traced one eyebrow with her fingertip.

He caught that wandering finger and kissed it. 'So I can get a chance to say some of the things I've been wanting to say for so long.'

'You don't have to.'

He stared into her smoky-blue eyes for a long time. And when he spoke finally it was a little unevenly. 'Yes, I do. So that there can never be any misunderstandings again. You're like no other lover I've ever had, Hillary. You're like no other person I've ever known. You're ... like a part of me. The heart of my heart. The crazy thing is, you always were ...'

'Don't,' she whispered, and smoothed away the lines of pain on his forehead.

'I had to say it ...'

'I think,' she said tremulously, still stroking his face, 'I'm glad you did. But now I think we have to put it all behind us and start again from here. You know what I'd like?'

'What would you like?'

'I'd like to be pregnant ... I think I'd like that very much. Reckon we're going the right way about it?' She looked into his eyes with a tiny, teasing smile on her lips.

Clive caught his breath and buried his face in her hair and they clung to each other for a long time. Then he let her go and gazed down at her and lifted a hand to touch her breasts. 'They do say, if at first you don't succeed, the thing to do is keep trying,' he murmured with the utmost gravity.

'Oh, I love the thought of that!'

Bea Selby turned the passage corner and was about to enter Hillary's bedroom when she stopped abruptly, spellbound.

Then she whisked herself away and there were sudden tears in her eyes, not only for the sheer beauty of what she had just seen—Clive and Hillary totally oblivious of anything but themselves, laughing tenderly at each other and about to embrace with an almost tangible aura of love encircling them—but tears of relief, too.

'Thank God,' she whispered, leaning back against the passage wall briefly. Then she pushed herself upright and walked away, shaking her head wryly. 'We're strange creatures!'

To be read with caution whilst sunbathing.

The Mills & Boon Holiday Pack contains four specially select-ed romances from some of our top authors and can be extremely difficult to put down.

But take care, because long hours under the summer sun, engrossed in hot passion can amount to a lot of sunburn.

So the next time you are filling your suitcase with the all-important Mills & Boon Holiday Pack, take an extra bottle of After Sun Lotion.

Just in case.

ROMANCE

ROMANCE

Next month's romances from Mills & Boon

Each month, you can choose from a world of variety in romance with Mills & Boon. These are the new titles to look out for next month.

A WILLING SURRENDER Robyn Donald
PRISONER Vanessa James
ESCAPE FROM THE HAREM Mary Lyons
CAPTURE A SHADOW Leigh Michaels
GLASS SLIPPERS AND UNICORNS Carole Mortimer
THE WAITING MAN Jeneth Murrey
THE LONELY SEASON Susan Napier
BODYCHECK Elizabeth Oldfield
WIN OR LOSE Kay Thorpe
SHADOW PRINCESS Sophie Weston
*SURRENDER, MY HEART Lindsay Armstrong
*WILD FOR TO HOLD Annabel Murray

Buy them from your usual paperback stockist, or write to: Mills & Boon Reader Service, P.O. Box 236, Thornton Rd, Croydon, Surrey CR9 3RU, England. Readers in South Africa-write to: Independent Book Services, Postbag X3010, Randburg, 2125, S. Africa.

*These two titles are available *only* from Mills & Boon Reader Service.

Mills & Boon
the rose of romance

The burning secrets of a girl's first love.

She was young and rebellious, fighting the restrictions imposed by her South American convent.

He was a doctor, dedicated to the people of his war-torn country.

Drawn together by a sensual attraction. Nothing should have stood in their way.

Yet a tragic secret was to keep them apart …

Following Hidden in the Flame's tremendous success last year here's another chance to read this passionate story.

W❂RLDWIDE

AVAILABLE FROM JUNE 1986. Price £2.50.